Study Guide for

Care Support Workers

Level 3
NVQ/SVQ in Care
Mandatory Group A and Option Group B Units

Stephen O'Kell
First Class Books, Inc.
P.O. Box 1, Portishead
Bristol, BS20 9 BR

Study Guide for

Care Support Workers

ISBN: 1-880246-10-4

Copyright © 1999
by First Class Books, Inc.

First Class Books

P.O. Box 1, Portishead
Bristol BS20 9BR

Phone: (01823) 323126
Fax: (01823) 321876

RECYCLED

Printed in the United States of America
on recyclable paper.

Introduction

The new, level 3 National Vocational Qualification/Scottish Vocational Qualification (NVQ/SVQ) in Care Award provides a set of performance standards for Care Support Workers from all occupational groups. The care standards specify the quality of performance in the workplace for those who deliver hands-on care. Achieving the standards develops competence for assisting care professionals in institutional and community settings.

The award consists of mandatory and optional units. Mandatory units are common to all the NVQ/SVQ in Care awards undertaken at level 3 and, therefore, must be completed by all candidates. Optional units are those which are most relevant to an individual's work role that a candidate can choose to complete an NVQ/SVQ award.

To achieve the full award (twelve units), a candidate must complete all five Mandatory Group A units plus seven optional units. At least four of the optional units must be chosen from Option Group B. If required, the remainder can be chosen from Option Group C (maximum 3 units). This workbook provides the underpinning knowledge relating to the five Mandatory Group A units and the thirteen Option Group B units of the level 3 NVQ/SVQ in Care award.

Contents

Module 1

Promoting Equality and Diversity

Promote equal opportunities and rights for all

Need-to-know words:

- abuse
- advocate
- adopted role
- ascribed role
- assault
- assertiveness
- battery
- challenging behaviour
- confidentiality
- defamation
- depersonalisation
- discrimination
- empathy
- false documentation
- halo effect
- institutionalisation
- label
- libel
- negligence
- noncompliance
- non-verbal communication
- paranoia
- prejudice
- prognosis
- right
- significant other
- slander
- stereotype
- stigma
- verbal communication

Objectives:

- Outline how to promote the rights of others.
- Highlight the potential for conflict between individual and organisational roles and responsibilities.
- Respect the personal beliefs and life choices of others.
- Recognise the various forms of discrimination and their effect on the provision of care.
- Describe how to promote equality in care environments.
- Explain the causes and effects of inequalities in health.
- Describe how to maintain confidentiality.
- Identify causes of challenging behaviour.
- Describe the different types of abuse and signs and symptoms of abuse.
- Utilise a model for analysing challenging behaviour.
- Outline how to care for people "at risk."

Module 1 Introduction

Module 1 relates directly to two units of the level 3 NVQ/SVQ Award in Care:

Unit O2: **Promote people's equality, diversity, and rights** is a mandatory group A unit that consists of three elements of competence:

- O2.1 Promote people's rights and responsibilities
- O2.2 Promote equality and diversity of people
- O2.3 Promote people's right to the confidentiality of information

Unit Z1: **Contribute to the protection of individuals from abuse** is also a mandatory group A unit which consists of three elements of competence:

- Z1.1 Contribute to minimising the level of abuse in environments
- Z1.2 Minimise the effects of abusive behaviour
- Z1.3 Contribute to monitoring individuals who are at risk from abuse

Part 1: Promoting Rights and Responsibilities (O2.1)

Promote and support individual rights and choices.

The **Universal Declaration of Human Rights** (United Nations, 1948) has had considerable impact throughout the world. The declaration includes the following rights:

- Recognition as a person before the law
- Education and employment
- Self-determination
- Life
- Not being subjected to medical experimentation without consent
- Social security
- Adequate standard of living including food, clothing, and housing

The **Declaration of Rights of Mentally Retarded Persons** (United Nations, 1971) recognised that people who have learning disabilities might not be adequately covered by the previous declaration. This declaration outlines rights for people who have learning disabilities.

They should:

- Have the same rights as other people, in so far as this is feasible
- Have a guardian (advocate) appointed if they cannot make their own decisions

The **Mental Health Act** (1983) addresses the following legal rights:

- Voting
- Entering hire purchase contracts
- Entering into marriage
- Having property and assets protected
- Having protection against cruelty and exploitation
- Writing to certain members of society

The **law of the land** gives citizens further rights:

- To vote
- To demonstrate
- To legal representation
- To protection from theft and physical harm

Exercise 1.1 ✐

Care in the Community guidelines were established by the Department of Health (1990) for local authorities to be responsible for planning the provision of community care services in their localities. Local authorities work in conjunction with the following:

- District health authorities

- Family health service authorities

- Local housing authorities

- Voluntary organisations

- Private sector care organisations

Community services have been established so that, where possible, people who need care in the community have a right to available services. Services include the following:

- A full assessment of needs and the delivery of a negotiated package of services to meet those needs

- Domiciliary, day, and respite services to enable people to live in their own homes, where feasible and sensible

- Practical support for families who provide care for relatives at home

- Residential care services for individuals who cannot cope on their own

The **Patient's Charter** clearly sets out people's rights to care and standards of service that should be provided by the NHS, GP, hospital, community, ambulance, dental, optical and pharmaceutical services. A health authority's performance in relation to the Patient's Charter standards is important because the Department of Health compares its performance to those of other health authorities and publicly reports on its findings in the form of performance league tables each year.

The Patient's Charter is eventually to be replaced by a new set of national standards and guidelines which will be backed by a National Institute for Clinical Excellence and a Commission for Health Improvement. The commission will have the power to intervene when health care is not available to acceptable standards (Department of Health, 1997).

Exercise 1.2

Promote and support the rights of each person in your care. Encourage them to express their needs and wishes. When individuals make choices, this encourages their independence.

- Stick to your promises, and inform people if you are going to be late.

- Be specific when providing options to clients. Let them know if the options are reduced. Explain why, and make a record of the transaction.

- If, for any reason, someone is unable to make choices, take the person's interests into account before making a choice for the person. You do this by consulting others (e.g. , advocate, friend, relative, significant other, interpreter) before you make the decision.

- Give a clear explanation when a person's request cannot be granted or must be restricted.

- Do not allow yourself or others to be manipulated.

- If you have concerns about offering choices, seek advice.

Some client groups are much more likely to be deprived of their rights to available services because of the effects of prejudice and because they may not actively seek services (e.g., gypsies, tramps, New-age travellers, some ethnic minorities). The emphasis for these groups must be on informing them of available services and ensuring accessibility to the services.

Responsibilities

A person's responsibilities are usually dependent on that individual's roles in life and in society as a whole. The following roles provide responsibilities for people which may be difficult for them to carry out when they are ill or disabled or require care:

- Family roles (e.g., father, sister, uncle, grandparent)

- Work roles (e.g., heavy lifting, typing)

- Legal roles (e.g., juror, guardian, law abiding citizen, tax payer)

- Societal roles (e.g., good neighbour, breadwinner)

- Religious roles (e.g., attending mass, fasting during Ramadan)

- Social roles (e.g., footballer, choir master, scout)

An inability to carry out any of the above ascribed or adopted roles can be very stressful for that person and any others who are dependent on that role being carried out.

Exercise 1.3

Sometimes there can be conflicts in people's roles and responsibilities. Following are examples:

- Between the different roles in a person's life (e.g., long hours at work may make it difficult to spend much time with the family).

- Between one's own rights and responsibilities (e.g., caring for a sick relative may prevent a person from continuing his or her education or gaining employment).

- Between the rights and responsibilities of different people (e.g., a nurse's responsibility to give medication and a patient's right to refuse it).

- Between the rights and responsibilities of individuals and organisations (e.g., the right for personal information to be kept confidential against an organisation's responsibility to ensure access to that information by a number of professionals).

Exercise 1.4

Individual Rights

It is essential that you promote the rights of all the people in your care. They must come first—usually before you and your employing organisation. Make sure that you know your organisations's policies relating to people's rights, including your responsibilities and the boundaries of action that you can take.

You need to be aware of your own values and beliefs so that you can ensure that they do not conflict with your expected work roles. If you have difficulties in this area (e.g., your work uniform does not conform to the requirements of your religion to cover parts of your body), consult your manager.

The promotion of individual rights can be achieved in a number of ways:

- Reminding individuals of their rights (e.g., welfare benefits)

- Identifying and assessing individuals who are incapacitated to make sure that they are receiving their rights, or advocating on their behalf when necessary (e.g., insisting that an individual does not have too many visitors when adequate rest is essential to the person's care)

- Ensuring that individuals who cannot speak up for themselves have interpreters or advocates to represent them and ensure that their rights are met

- Ensuring that information relating to rights and resources or support are made available to people (e.g., providing information leaflets, showing people how to use the complaints system, referring people to colleagues or departments where relevant information is available, directing individuals to the Citizens Advice Bureau)

- Informing your manager when you notice that a person's rights are being infringed, especially if local policies are not being followed or when there may be legal implications

- Ensuring that you complete all relevant records relating to people's rights (e.g., complaint forms, accident forms)

- Gently challenging people when their choices of action infringe on the rights of others (e.g., requesting an angry relative, who is complaining about the quality of care, to accompany you to the office so that she does not frighten or disturb others)

Exercise 1.5 ✏

Part 2: Promoting Equality and Diversity (02.2)

Everyone deserves to be treated with respect and dignity.

One of the things that we all do when we meet people for the first time is to make assumptions about them. Our assumptions will be based on whether the people are similar to, or different from, ourselves. Depending on your own values, attitudes, and beliefs (value position), you may view the differences positively or negatively. A value position acts like a filter in the perception of facts about others.

Personal Beliefs and Identity

To respect the personal beliefs and identity of others, you need to be aware of your own value position. You will also need to develop the ability to shift your (value) position in order to see things from the point of view of others—putting yourself in their shoes. This will enable you to appreciate the different perspectives (values, attitudes, and beliefs) of others so that you can develop empathy when caring for these people.

You will be expected to recognise and support individual beliefs and preferences. Actively encourage people in your care to express their beliefs, wishes, and views, as long as they do not interfere with the rights of others. Personal beliefs and preferences are important. Therefore, acknowledge individuals' beliefs about self, race, religion, politics, culture, ethics, and sexuality by responding in a manner that is supportive.

Also, be aware of your own beliefs if they are likely to cause conflict in the provision of care (e.g., if you are a strict Catholic, you will not want to be involved in abortions). Inform your supervisor if your care role conflicts with your religious or other beliefs.

Beliefs and preferences affect the foods people eat, the clothing they wear, how they worship, and other aspects of daily living. You can support an individual's beliefs in a variety of ways.

- Be sensitive to each person's needs.

- Support the right to practice individual beliefs.

- Make sure your speech and actions do not offend others.

- Address individuals by their preferred name and title.

- Take into consideration beliefs and lifestyles when planning care.

- Be respectful of each person's customs and possessions.

- Show interest in each person's beliefs.

- Be willing to listen when a person wants to talk.

- Never question or make fun of another person's beliefs.

- Never try to force your beliefs on another person.

- Never ask non-Christians for their "Christian names." (Ask for their first names.)

Exercise 1.6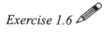

Religious Customs

Be familiar with religious customs (e.g., Sikh men must leave their hair unshorn and wear a turban). The more you know, the less likely you are to accidentally offend someone. People may have religious items in their possession (such as rosaries or prayer books). If you must move these items, handle them with respect.

Holidays: Be aware of days that are celebrated with special rituals (e.g., Passover for Jews). People may need extra help dressing for holidays or they may

need privacy for certain rituals (e.g., confession or prayer).

Foods: Some religions forbid certain foods. Know what is not allowed, and offer other choices. (For example, most Moslems and Hindus do not eat pork or beef; they only eat meat that has been killed a special way). Be aware of special times that people may fast (go without food) or eat only certain foods (e.g., Ramadan for Moslems).

Clothing: Some religions have certain articles of clothing that must be worn or treated with respect (e.g., devout Moslem women may only leave their eyes uncovered in public).

Medical Treatments: Be aware of any medical treatments that are not allowed because of religious beliefs (e.g., blood transfusions for Jehovah's Witness followers).

Clergy: If an individual wants to see a member of clergy, make sure all relevant people are informed. Provide privacy whenever a member of clergy visits.

Death: Different religions have different rules governing what to do with a body after death (e.g., followers of Islam should not be touched by non-Moslems after death; if they have to be touched, wear gloves).

Exercise 1.7 🖉

Discrimination

Always provide quality care, regardless of a person's background, beliefs, race, ethnicity, gender, sexuality, age, mental or physical ability. Your personal beliefs and preferences should not affect the quality of service you provide. Your personal beliefs can affect your behaviour in a variety of direct and indirect ways. Be aware of legislation and local organisational policies that prohibit discriminatory practice (unfair treatment). The Disability Discrimination Act (1995) makes it unlawful to discriminate unjustifiably against disabled people.

The ways in which you communicate with people should reflect your care role and the power invested in that role. Therefore, if you have any feelings of hostility toward population groups, be careful not to express those feelings at work. If necessary, seek advice on how to deal with your feelings.

There are different types of discrimination. *Overt discrimination* operates when a person is openly discriminating (e.g., advertising that your club is only open to white-skinned people). *Covert discrimination* is much more difficult to prove. An example is all managers of an organisation who have risen through the ranks are males, when the majority of employees are females.

Appropriate discrimination can take the form of refusing to employ convicted child abusers to work in a children's home, or not allowing children with epilepsy to play on the high climbing frame. *Inappropriate* (but not illegal) *discrimination* can take the form of employing only people under the age of 55 years into senior management posts. Another example is accepting unnecessary rude and aggressive behaviour from a disabled person, just because he or she is disabled.

Exercise 1.8

To promote equality, it is important to recognise and accept other people's beliefs and lifestyles (even when they clash with your own). Every individual has the right to equality and an acceptable quality of life, regardless of the person's past history and beliefs.

Stereotyping and Prejudice

Many groups of people have stereotypes attached to them on the basis that people from the same groups have similar characteristics or traits (e.g., Scots are mean, redheads are fiery, accountants are boring). Therefore, people sometimes attribute a variety of qualities or labels to an individual that are radically wrong.

Some stereotypes have positive values attached to them and some have negative values attached, referred to as a *stigma*. A person with a stigma is often a target for discrimination.

In the care sector, there are several client groups that carry a stigma (e.g., the elderly, the disabled, the mentally ill, people who have learning disabilities). This stigma leads to the *halo effect* where there is a strong tendency for these people to conform to other people's negative expectations of them. People's negative expectations tend to affect the quality of their interactions with these stigmatised individuals, further reducing chances for improved relationships.

Equal Opportunities

The Equal Opportunities Commission (1986) outlined 10 aspects that should be written into organisational policies if they are to become equal opportunity employers. The policies should include the following:

1. Definitions of direct and indirect discrimination, victimisation, and sexual harassment

2. A statement of the organisation's commitment to equal opportunities

3. The name of the officer(s) responsible for ensuring the policy is carried out

4. Details for how the policy is to be carried out

5. An obligation upon employees to respect and act in accordance with the policy

6. Procedures for dealing with complaints of discrimination

7. Examples of unlawful practices

8. Details of monitoring and reviewing procedures

9. A commitment to remove barriers to equal opportunity

10. Provision of equal opportunities training

Protect yourself and others from discrimination by taking appropriate action. Following are examples:

- Provide feedback to anyone who has been discriminatory; explain the effects and consequences of his or her actions.

- Offer support and guidance to people who have been discriminated against and to those at risk from discrimination.

- Make a formal complaint about any discrimination you encounter, or support others in doing so.

Exercise 1.9

Health and Inequalities

There is no universal agreement on a definition of health. Defined negatively, health is the absence of ill health or disability with no barriers to being able to function normally from a biological perspective. The most famous example of a positive definition of health is *"a state of complete physical, mental, and social well-being, and not merely the absence of disease or infirmity"* (World Health Organisation, 1994). The strength of this definition is that it draws attention to the psychological and social aspects of health, rather than focusing primarily on the physical aspects of health.

There is general agreement that health is determined by a whole range of influences from genetic inheritance, personal behaviour, family and social circumstances, the physical and social environment. Therefore, action for improvements in the nation's health must be shared between individuals and the government.

In contrast to these definitions of health, mortality (death) rates are the most commonly used measure of health. The assumption is that if rates of premature death are high, then rates of illness are also high. This is because there are strong links between death rates, illness, and disability. However, there is much ill health which does not lead to death (e.g., disabling conditions such as arthritis and mental illness).

Exercise 1.10

The Nation's Health

The difficulty that the government and local health and social care providers encounter in meeting people's care needs is finding the right balance between what should be done in terms of care needs, what can be done at a practical level, and what can be afforded.

"Add years to life and life to years" is the aim of the White Paper entitled *Health of the Nation* (Department of Health, 1992). The idea is to combine public policies, healthy surroundings, lifestyles, and high-quality health services to improve the health of the nation. There is also a focus on monitoring people's health and researching ways to improve health. The aim is to secure improvements in the health of the population.

Five key areas for action have been chosen:

- Coronary heart disease and stroke: e.g., to reduce death rates from coronary heart disease and strokes in people under 65 by at least 40 percent by the year 2000

- Cancers: e.g., to reduce the death rate from breast cancer by at least 25 percent by the year 2000

- Mental illness: e.g., to reduce the suicide rate by at least 15 percent by the year 2000

- HIV/AIDS and sexual health: e.g., to reduce by at least 50 percent, the rate of pregnancy amongst the under 16s by the year 2000

- Accidents: e.g., to reduce the death rate for accidents among people aged 65 and over by at least 33 percent by the year 2005

In addition, four risk factors are included:

- Smoking: e.g., to reduce consumption of cigarettes by at least 40 percent by the year 2000

- Diet and nutrition: e.g., to reduce the proportion of men and women aged 16-44 who are obese by at least 25 percent and 33 percent respectively by the year 2005

- Blood pressure: e.g., to reduce the mean systolic blood pressure in the adult population by at least five by the year 2005

- HIV/AIDS: e.g., to reduce the percentage of drug misusers who report sharing drug injecting equipment in the previous four weeks to no more than 10 percent by the year 2000

The previous areas were chosen because they are major causes of premature death or avoidable ill-health. Also, effective interventions are possible, offering scope for significant improvements in health.

Exercise 1.11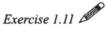

Inequalities in Health

It is generally agreed that health is affected by social and economic factors such as low income and poor housing. The fact that people who are socio-economically disadvantaged suffer a heavier burden of illness and have higher mortality rates than their better-off counterparts has been well researched over the years (Robinson & Elkan, 1996).

Occupational class is a widely used indicator of socio-economic status. One widely used measure of occupational class is the Registrar General's classification scale as follows:

I   Professional (e.g., lawyer, doctor, accountant)

II   Intermediate (e.g., teacher, nurse, manager)

IIIN   Skilled non-manual (e.g., typist, shop assistant)

IIIM   Skilled manual (e.g., miner, bus driver, cook)

IV   Partly-skilled manual (e.g., farm workers, bus conductor)

V   Unskilled manual (e.g., cleaner, labourer)

This scale brings together people with similar skills and lifestyles by classifying them according to the occupation of the head of the household. The occupational groups correlate fairly well with other aspects of social position such as education and income.

Exercise 1.12 📝

Although the reasons for health variations are known, it is difficult to achieve health improvements by health care intervention when people are reluctant to change their lifestyles (Department of Health, 1995). Therefore, each district health authority is expected to map out the levels of social deprivation that exist in their districts. These measures form the basis for funding health care and include factors such as the following:

- Percent elderly living alone
- Percent social class V
- Percent unemployed
- Percent one-parent families
- Percent in overcrowded households
- Percent ethnic minorities

The District Health Authorities are then expected to do the following:

- Identify population groups who suffer the worst health and target resources accordingly.
- Overcome barriers to accessing health services for all groups of people.
- Evaluate the effectiveness of the health interventions that they provide.

- Work in alliance with other bodies including local authorities and the voluntary care sector.

Health services are then planned and delivered to meet local need. In reality, if real health gains are to be achieved, coordinated action is needed from a number of government departments in order to achieve reductions in homelessness, increases in income support, reductions in air and water pollution, improvements in health, safety at work, etc.

Unfortunately, shortages of health care funding mean that health care is rationed in all parts of the country. This results, for example, in health care for patients who are dying, being made available for only four weeks in some parts of the country. The alternative for these people is to seek means-tested care from the private and voluntary health-care sectors.

Exercise 1.13

The net result is that many health inequalities have been documented in terms of the distribution of health problems and the use of health-care services throughout the United Kingdom. It is thought that geographical variations in health are underpinned by differences in the social-class profiles between different regions of the United Kingdom. This is primarily seen in Scotland and the North of England where there are greater concentrations of the lower social classes. This has resulted in the following health variations:

- The mortality rate of men (20-64 years) is 7.86 per 1000 population in Central Clydeside, compared to a rate of 4.37 per 1000 in East Anglia.

- For all major causes of death, mortality is greater in social class V than social class I.

- There would be 42,000 fewer deaths each year if the death rate of people who have manual jobs were the same as those in non-manual occupations.

- A child from social class V is twice as likely to die before the age of 15 than a child who has a social class I father.

It has been estimated that since the 1950s inequalities in health between the upper and lower social classes have been widening. This may be due to the fact that those in the higher social classes enjoy better access to better health care including hospital services, preventive services, and primary-care services, than those in the lower social classes. That is, those who need the most care tend to receive the least.

In order to achieve equal opportunities in using health and social services and achieve equal health outcomes, different population groups should receive the following:

- Equal access to services (e.g., physical access to buildings, languages used on leaflets)

- Equal shares of services (e.g., ensuring that people's expressed needs are listened to, when planning and distributing services)

- Equal treatment by the services—not necessarily the *same* services (e.g., although people require the same quality of service, this may mean providing different people with different services, according to need)

Exercise 1.14

Part 3: Maintaining Confidentiality (02.3)

Ensure right of access before disclosing personal details.

In the course of your work, you will need to handle health and care records. A person's ability to speak freely to a health or social care worker stems from trust in the care professional's duty of confidentiality. The confidential nature of these records cannot be overstressed. Information about the people in your care is very private.

Individuals have a right to expect that information given in confidence will be used only for the purpose for which it was given and that it will not be released to others without their consent. Confidential information includes all medical information—diagnosis, prognosis, and treatment—and everything related to personal, social, and financial data. The person-in-charge of your clinical area is responsible for maintaining the security of all health and care records.

You have both a legal and moral responsibility to maintain confidentiality about personal information. Information is disclosed only to those who have the right and the need to know, according to statutory or agency policies. Never disclose information unless you have proof of the enquirer's identity and right of access. Unauthorized disclosure or misuse of information contained in health and care records is a serious breach of discipline and could lead to your dismissal.

Make sure that you know your organisation's policies that pertain to your role relating to confidentiality, access, and transmission of information. This includes knowing the records that can be accessed by people receiving care and those to which they should not have access. For example, it is appropriate that a patient/client should have access to his own plan of care, but not to budget sheets or the accident book for a particular establishment.

Exercise 1.15 🖎

The United Kingdom Central Council for Nursing, Midwifery, and Health Visiting (1987) provides general guidelines on confidentiality, emphasizing accountability for confidential information obtained in the course of practice.

The **Data Protection Act** (Home Office, 1998) establishes the principles for managing electronically-held information and structured paper-based, client records. It also gives individuals the right of access to information held about them on computers. These principles specify that personal data must meet the following criteria:

- Processed fairly and lawfully with special care being taken with sensitive, personal data

- Obtained only for lawful purposes, as specified in the Act

- Be adequate, relevant, and not excessive for the specified purposes

- Be accurate and, where necessary, kept up-to-date

- Kept no longer than necessary for the specified purposes

- Ensure an individual's rights (e.g., making a person's records available to him or her upon request)

- Properly protected against loss of disclosure

- Not be transferred to countries outside the European Economic Community

The Act also clearly specifies a number of offences under the Act. Offences include unlawfully obtaining or selling personal data, unlawfully accessing data via a third party, and unlawfully disclosing information to others.

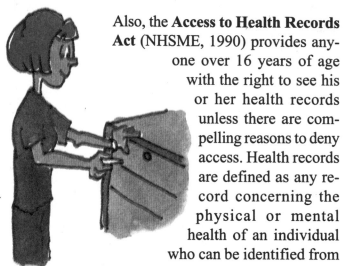

Also, the **Access to Health Records Act** (NHSME, 1990) provides anyone over 16 years of age with the right to see his or her health records unless there are compelling reasons to deny access. Health records are defined as any record concerning the physical or mental health of an individual who can be identified from the information recorded (e.g., details of investigations, diagnosis, treatment, or examinations). The Act allows for individuals to apply to access their own health records. This is achieved by writing to the holder of the record (e.g., doctor or health authority). The application must be fully processed within 40 days and a fee up to 10£ plus the cost of postage and copying may be charged (unless the applicant simply reads the records on the spot).

Exercise 1.16

Follow the **Code of Practice**:

- Records should be handled only by staff authorised to handle them as part of their duties.

- The contents of health and care records should never, under any circumstances, be communicated to persons who are not authorised to have them.

- The contents of records should be discussed only with persons who need to know in order to carry out their care roles.

- If you find someone who is unknown to you who is handling or reading health or care records, you should challenge the person for proof of identity and authority to handle the records.

- Record stores should be kept locked when not in use, with the key being held by an authorised person.

- Electronic access codes to databases should be kept secret by the carers who have been given the authority to use the codes.

Requests for Health and Care Records

The interchange of health and care records throughout a district or within an organisation will normally be undertaken by staff who know each other. Other requests should be handled in the following way:

- Requests from outside your organisation or district should, if possible, be in writing. If this is not possible, you need to contact the person-in-charge. You should always obtain the name, job, and telephone number of the person requesting the record so that the person's identity and authority can be verified.

- Requests by patients should not be dealt with by telephone. They should be asked to apply in writing, providing their reasons for wanting the information.

- Requests for information by relatives and others (e.g., insurance companies) should only be accepted if the patient/client or guardian gives permission in writing.

- You may need to complete a tracer card so that your organisation can keep track of its records.

- If records are to be sent outside your organisation or district, you may be required to send photocopies, rather than the originals.

- All records that are being transferred should be sealed in an envelope before being despatched.

Exercise 1.17

Breaching Confidentiality

There may be times when you are told information that needs to be passed on to someone else for action (e.g., when someone is at risk). You will need to check your organisation's policies relating to this issue. When you must pass on information that has been given to you in confidence, carefully explain to the person who told you that you may have to share the information with others (e.g., when you find out that a person is a substance abuser or is contemplating suicide). Explain the reasons why the information should be shared with others and who, precisely, will have access to the information.

In addition, conflict can arise between confidentiality and the legal need to share information with other parties (e.g., the police). The Data Protection Act allows personal data to be disclosed to certain parties when it is essential for the purposes of preventing or detecting a crime or for the apprehension or prosecution of offenders. Confidentiality can be inadvertently breached when members of staff are not careful with confidential information. This most often occurs in the following ways:

- Talking about clients in corridors, on public transport, etc., where other people can hear

- Leaving case notes lying around where unauthorised people can simply pick them up and read them

- Leaving personal information unattended on computer screens for unauthorised people to read

The following guidelines protect confidential information.

- Lock case notes away.

- Blank out computer screens, or turn the screens so that unauthorised people cannot see them.

- Courteously point out to the people concerned that they are breaching confidentiality, that they should refrain from doing so, and that they are putting their jobs at risk if they are caught or reported.

- If confidentiality is being blatantly breached, despite warnings, report the people concerned to an appropriate manager.

If you see or hear a breach of confidentiality, take action immediately. Inform your manager if your part of the organisation maintains, stores, and retrieves records in a way that appears to conflict with good practice. If you need advice, contact the nominated information officer for your organisation. If you suspect that there has been abuse of confidential information or if you have any concerns about confidentiality, contact your manager.

Part 4: Protecting Individuals from Abuse (Z1)

Help to minimise the risk of abuse.

It is important to understand that there is always a reason for a person's behaviour. People receiving care are often adjusting to changes in their lifestyles that affect them physically, emotionally, and socially. Never express anger or irritation toward the people in your care.

Today's faster pace of life and social problems results in more people suffering from the effects of stress. Individuals cope with their frustrations in different ways. Some people take out their anger on everyone; others may be quiet and withdrawn. Some people blame all of their problems on others; others blame themselves. Some deny there is a problem; others try to find a reason for everything.

Your attitude affects their behaviour and well-being. Understanding and accepting your own feelings is important. Whenever you feel frustrated, try to understand why you feel that way. If you are unable to cope with your feelings, seek advice.

Exercise 1.18 🖉

To manage abusive behaviour, the emphasis must be on prevention and de-escalation of the situation before aggression occurs. Abuse aimed at care staff is often caused by an action or failure to carry out an action by a member of the care staff.

In addition, avoid personal behaviour which can provoke or escalate abuse.

- Avoid using a tone of voice that is nagging, demanding, or showing boredom.

- Do not break off conversations without apologising, and always try to return to a conversation after an interruption.

- Do not overreact by using abusive language or issuing threats.

- Avoid getting into arguments.

- Do not ignore questions or the people posing them.

- Try to remain calm.

- Although abuse is personal in nature, do not take it personally.

- Accept apologies gracefully.

- Do not use phrases such as "calm down" or "don't be silly" as these talk down to the person and belittle the problem.

- Avoid laughing, chatting, reading magazines, etc., in front of people who are waiting.

- Use appropriate non-verbal communication. Do not shrug shoulders, raise eyebrows, point, commence clock watching, stand with hands on hips, arms folded across the chest, etc.

- Do not point at, or push, an abuser.

- Maintain a normal distance between yourself and the abuser.

- Try to get the abuser to sit down and talk.

Exercise 1.19 🖉

Challenging Behaviour

Sometimes people are uncooperative, demanding, threatening, rude, or stubborn. Try to find the underlying cause of the behaviour. Some common concerns that affect people's behaviour include the following:

- Anxiety, fear
- Change in lifestyle
- Health problems
- Pain
- Grief
- Unmet needs
- Depression
- Loneliness
- Physical and mental changes
- Longing for the "old days"
- Lack of understanding
- Unmet expectations
- Family problems
- Lack of self-esteem
- Religious concerns
- Lack of sleep or rest
- Financial concerns
- Loss of independence

Occasionally, people become angry or upset about the situation of their loved one. Even though it can be difficult for you, try to be understanding and supportive of these people.

Abuse in the form of discrimination can occur if people are labelled as "difficult," "awkward," or a "problem." Sometimes carers try to avoid these people, and this can make them more abusive.

Exercise 1.20 🖉

Be aware that timing and mood are important variables which can make people react differently to the same stimulus at different times. For example, a person might be happy to listen to a long-winded joke most of the time, but it might make the person quite angry if you try telling the joke when he or she is rushing to make an appointment or when feeling ill.

Be aware of other factors that can cause challenging behaviour:

- The influence of alcohol or drugs (prescribed or illegal)

- Mental illness, especially when there are feelings of paranoia

- The environment (e.g., noisy, dirty, crowded, hot)

- The affect of having to wait and/or queue for long lengths of time

- Your dress and professional manner, (representing unacceptable "authority")

- Your irritating behaviour (e.g., showing boredom, interrupting others' conversations)

Exercise 1.21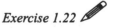

Challenging behaviour can often be reduced by offering advice and support, as appropriate. Help people understand why their inappropriate behaviour may be seen as abusive. Use your interpersonal skills to deflect people's energies into useful activity rather than escalating conflict.

Abuse

Abuse refers to any situation where a person's human or legal rights are refused, restricted, or curtailed. People who are close to a person being abused often do not know and will not allow themselves to believe that it is happening. They may become very upset about the suspicions of care staff.

Abuse can take many forms and be short-term or long-term. It can be difficult to identify. For example, when does corporal punishment of a child become physical abuse, and when does a husband's bad temper become psychological abuse?

Abuse can be categorised according to the abuser:

- Self-abuse (e.g., taking illegal drugs, purposeful self-injury)

- Other abuse (e.g., child abuse, granny bashing)

Abuse can also be categorised according to the nature of the abuse that has taken place.

- Physical abuse (e.g., physical injuries from an attack or injuries caused by lack of an awareness of danger)

- Sexual abuse (e.g., rape, indecent assault, allowing a child to watch blue movies)

- Psychological abuse (e.g., creating anxiety over a period of time by the use of threats, not allowing a person to meet other people, institutionalisation)

Exercise 1.22

Signs and Symptoms of Abuse

It is possible for the signs and symptoms of abuse to occur when there has been no abuse. Suspicion usually occurs when several of the signs and symptoms are noticed at once and over time. This may be linked to explanations that are inconsistent with the injury or behaviour. Many of the short-term effects of abuse are well-documented. However, the long-term effects can be more traumatic, especially if the victim exhibits behaviour that makes other people reject him or her.

Physical signs and symptoms:

- Multiple bruises/bruises of different ages

- Bruises on the face, especially around the mouth and ears

- Splits on the inside of lips

- Fingertip bruising (resulting from having been forcibly gripped)

- Bite marks (usually an oval bruise with a gap at each side)

- Odd-shaped bruises that outline the shape of the weapon used

- Scratch marks and bruises in difficult-to-injure places (e. g., inner thigh, inner or upper arm)

- Burns and scalds (cigarette burns cause a round mark or scar one to one and one-half centimetres across)

- Injuries and infections of the genitals

- General signs of neglect (including poor standards of hygiene and general nutrition)

- Munchausen syndrome by proxy (where the parent deliberately fabricates a child's symptoms in order to obtain surgery for the child)

Psychological signs and symptoms:

- Withdrawal and depression (avoiding eye contact, passivity, no spontaneous smiles)

- Inappropriate/unacceptable behaviour (avoidance or attention-seeking behaviour, tantrums, aggression)

- Anxiety (jumpy, tense, "frightened eyes")

- Impaired capacity to enjoy life

- Symptoms of psychiatric illness

Whether a person is abused in an isolated incident or over a prolonged period of time by one or many people, it is impossible to forecast what the long-term effects will be.

Exercise 1.23 ✎

Managing Abuse

Whenever serious abuse is suspected, a person can be admitted to hospital or taken to a "place of safety" for observation so that a more comprehensive assessment can be carried out.

The most important aspects of caring for people who have been abused include the following:

- Recognising the signs and symptoms of abuse

- Making accurate records of what you observe or what is reported by the client

- Informing an appropriate person of any concerns that you may have

- Ensuring that you know the plan of care for the abused person (this may include monitoring the person's whereabouts, placing restrictions on the person's movements, or restricting access to the person by potential visitors)

- Offering advice to the person on how to avoid or minimise the level of abuse

Exercise 1.24 ✎

Minimising Disruptive Behaviour

Try to minimise the negative effects of challenging behaviour. To do this, it is essential that you understand the cause of challenging behaviour before attempting to do anything to prevent or manage it (Poyner & Warne, 1988).

The model on the following page allows for an analysis to be made of all incidents of challenging behaviour. It consists of a carer interacting with a care recipient in a care environment to produce an outcome (challenging behaviour).

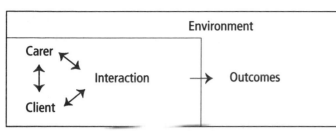

Model for Understanding Challenging Behaviour

The Carer

The characteristics of the carer can have a significant effect on the outcomes of care provision.

- Appearance and first impressions are important in any job involving encounters with the public. For example, a uniform can prevent some people from being abusive but may stimulate others to be abusive.

- Tolerance to stress may be important for your success in dealing with difficult interactions (e.g., your ability to control a group of boisterous children can be impaired if you are stressed by illness or work overload).

- Experienced staff have usually experienced similar situations, and the expectation is that they are more likely to handle challenging behaviour more effectively.

- Gender inevitably has an influence on challenging behaviour. For example, a woman might find it easier than a man to calm down an angry man, although women tend to feel more vulnerable to attack in certain situations.

- Personality and temperament of the carer affect behaviour. Some carers appear to be naturally better at handling difficult situations, usually because they have good interpersonal skills.

- Attitude toward people who need care and their families, and attitude to the job role tend to have an effect on how a carer behaves toward the people in his or her care.

- Expectations that carers have about their jobs influence their ability to handle difficult situations. For example, a carer who always expects people to conform to the plan of care is likely to cause anger and resentment in people who do not agree with their planned care.

Exercise 1.25 ✐

The behaviour of the carer can also have a significant impact on the level of abuse experienced.

- **Treat people with respect and dignity.** Do not "talk down" to people. Appear confident and concerned; avoid pat responses (e.g., "Everything will be alright"). Evaluate your own performance during interactions with people who are being abusive.

- **Maintain personal control of your feelings.** Remain calm, regardless of the situation. Showing your anger or displeasure at another person is likely to escalate the conflict.

- **Be honest with people.** Although it is important to control your anger, it is sometimes necessary to reveal your personal feelings. Communicate openly and effectively to promote acceptance and trust.

- **Provide face-saving alternatives.** Be willing to bargain and compromise by providing care alternatives from which a person can choose. This promotes a willingness to accept the care being provided. For example, a person complaining about the timing of meals could be offered alternative eating arrangements.

- **Set limits to behaviour.** Communicate clear messages about what is expected. Be consistently firm, and be assertive where necessary, (e.g., asking a person to stop smoking in a room that is clearly marked with "no smoking" signs).

- **Promote expression of feelings.** Allow and acknowledge feelings of anger or fear, and encourage the safe expression of those feelings. When appropriate, allowing a person the chance to "let off steam" may prevent the problem from escalating to violence.

- **Monitor people's behaviour**. The care provider continually assesses the environment so that he or she can choose the right moment and right manner to intervene. Monitoring involves recognising patterns of behaviour and getting to know the people who are receiving care. Especially important is being sensitive to non-verbal behaviours exhibited by both yourself and others.

- **Provide time to calm down.** Give a person time to calm down or to talk through the problem. Getting the person to describe the problem helps to refocus thinking on the problem rather than on acting out the anger, and it often provides the essential "cooling down period."

Exercise 1.26

The Client

The characteristics of the client can also have a significant effect on the outcomes of care provision.

- Personality and temperament of the care recipient affect behaviour. Some environments have to be set up specifically for care recipients who are likely to exhibit challenging behaviour (e.g., acute psychiatric units, substance abuse units, welfare benefit offices).

- Temporary conditions affect care, such as care recipients who are under the influence of drugs or alcohol or who are suffering from an illness or are distressed.

- Negative or uncertain expectations of the interaction to come can impact the situation. For example, a daughter expects that her father cannot be provided with care to meet his needs, and she is deeply concerned that he cannot remain in his own home.

- Immaturity can be a problem; children cannot be expected to control their emotions and behaviour.

Exercise 1.27

The Environment

Environment is the total context in which the care service is delivered. Each environment has factors which have an effect on incidents of challenging behaviour. Consider the following factors:

- Working alone: Home visits by health and social services staff are more difficult because the carers are guests in people's homes, and there is no back-up if things start to go wrong.

- Job location: Locally-based services are usually better able to respond sympathetically to difficult situations because they are aware of local issues. A person who provides services in a very rough area of town is more likely to encounter aggressive behaviour.

- Cash or drugs being carried: Carers are potential targets for robbers.

- Waiting and queuing: These are two of the many hassles with which the public has to cope.

- Time: People are more likely to be drunk at certain times of the day, and children are more likely to be on the streets at certain times of the day/week.

- Territory: People feel more comfortable on their own territory. This can affect the chances of challenging behaviour occurring.

- Room design: This includes room temperature, available space, seating arrangements, decorations, and furniture, etc. High room temperatures are much more likely to make people drowsy, irritable, and aggressive.

Exercise 1.28

The Interaction

If a person believes that he or she is being treated in an unfair or unreasonable way, it is not unusual for challenging behaviour to occur. Challenging behaviour can vary between difficult-to-handle behaviours (e.g., non-compliance, verbal abuse, spitting) to physical assault and violence.

If you are monitoring and recording a person's behaviour, try not to make it obvious, or you may get inaccurate results and/or make matters worse. Make accurate and complete records of all incidents of challenging behaviour.

Assertiveness refers to your ability to express your views in a clear, confident, and direct manner without denying the rights of others. Assertive behaviour is always preferable to passive or aggressive behaviour. Your clear, confident, and direct manner means that you can resolve problems without resorting to threats or manipulation. It also allows you to handle criticisms and uncertainty calmly. Furthermore, assertion can help you to refuse requests without feeling guilty or to ask for help when it is needed, without feeling inadequate.

The following assertion techniques can be used as a means of handling abusive and aggressive behaviour (Wondrak, 1989):

- Self-disclosure: Admitting that you are afraid.

- Partial agreement: Agreeing with part of a person's criticism (e.g., "Yes, I could have handled the situation a little better, but I am happy with the way things have turned out.")

- Gentle confrontation: Confronting a person in an attempt to uncover the reason for the abusive behaviour (e.g., "I am sorry. I did not mean to upset you by opening all the upstairs windows. What is the problem?")

- Side stepping: Agreeing fully with a person's criticism (e.g., "Yes, it was silly to close all the windows when it is so hot.")

- Being specific: Keeping what you have to say as specific as possible and avoiding unnecessary waffle (e.g., "John, I notice you keep kicking Jane under the table.")

Exercise 1.29

Understand your employer's policies regarding the management of aggression and violence. It is the employer's duty under the Health and Safety at Work Act (1974) to ensure that the work environment is as safe as possible for employees. Examples include visible security systems for buildings where appropriate, adequate staffing, and appropriate training to handle aggression and violence (Health and Safety Commission, 1987).

Exercise 1.30

Monitoring "At Risk" Individuals

It is your duty to report all complaints and any suspected abuse. In addition, it is your legal responsibility to respect people's rights and to protect them from harm (e.g., assault, battery, defamation, false documentation, negligence). Legal action may result from abuse or failure to report suspected abuse.

The most common type of abuse is child abuse. Each area of the country has local professional guidelines for referring children who are suspected of being abused. Your point of referral will probably be to discuss your concerns with your manager, who will decide whether to refer the matter to a statutory agency.

Child abuse may not be the only type of abuse that you come across. If any person in your care complains about having been abused or if you suspect abuse, report your evidence immediately to the person-in-charge. Make a detailed written record in your own handwriting while details are still fresh in your memory. The handwritten record should be retained (even if the report is eventually typed) as it can be used as evidence in court.

If a person in your care needs protection from abuse, be sure that you know the care plan and any rules or regulations that pertain to the situation. This includes ensuring that you know of any people in your care who are at risk.

Exercise 1.31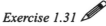

Caring For "At-Risk" People

Ensure the care plan explicitly states the level of supervision or observation needed for the person who is at risk. Some care plans have a necessary and appropriate element of risk which has been agreed by the care team. An example would be allowing a person to travel to the day centre without supervision when there is a slight risk that he or she might get lost.

Report any significant changes in the person's physical or mental condition immediately. Understand all legal and organisational policies and referral systems concerned with the types of abuse from which your client group are at risk.

Often there are other care agencies involved when there are people at risk. Because of the implications of potential legal action, it is essential that the various agencies keep accurate records and communicate with each other.

There may be times when you learn that someone (who may or may not be a client) is at risk. Carefully explain to the person who told you that you may have to share the information with others. Where possible, the information should be checked for accuracy. If you have any concerns about dealing with abuse at work, seek advice.

Exercise 1.32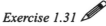

Summary

The personal characteristics that you bring to your role as a carer are important—personality, attitude, temperament, expectations, appearance, etc. The role requires a sincere desire to help and protect clients. Everyone deserves to be treated with respect and dignity regardless of beliefs, personal choices, race, gender, age, physical and mental abilities. Your responsibilities as a carer include promoting equality, supporting diversity, maintaining confidentiality, minimising abuse, and monitoring those at risk to ensure ethical and legal rights are upheld.

Check Your Knowledge and Understanding

1. A young mother attends a clinic for counselling with her six-month-old son. You notice that the child has a number of linear bruises to his lower back and buttocks. The mother says the bruises are a result of falls. You know the woman and suspect that the child is being abused by her common-law husband. What would you do?

   a) Immediately inform the woman that you think the child has been beaten and that you are going to inform the child protection officer.

   b) Inform the person-in-charge of the clinic about the situation.

   c) Decide to forget what you have seen on the grounds of confidentiality.

   d) Wait until you have finished work, and make an anonymous phone call to the child protection officer.

2. A person who has been a patient on your ward turns up one day. He confides that he is going to take the surgeon to court for botching his operation. He asks you to supply him with a copy of his computerised records so that they can be used as evidence in court. What would you do?

   a) Simply print a copy of the person's medical record, and give it to him.

   b) Refuse to supply him with a copy of his medical records on the grounds that patients are not allowed to see their records.

   c) Inform the nurse in charge of the situation, and let the nurse deal with it.

   d) Contact the surgeon concerned so that he or she can come down to the ward to deal with this person's request.

3. Your boss, a married man, has started sexually harassing you by making occasional lewd suggestions and telling filthy jokes. You have politely asked him to stop, but he simply replied that he was only joking and walked away. The harassment has continued. What should you do?

   a) Slap his face the next time he sexually harasses you.

   b) Ask for a transfer or look for another job.

   c) Ignore your manager in the hope that he will stop harassing you.

   d) Report your manager's behaviour to the personnel department.

4. There are times when it is appropriate to breach confidentiality. Under which of the following situations would a breach of confidentiality be appropriate?

   a) A client informs you that she is contemplating suicide.

   b) A client informs you that he has been sexually abusing his step-daughter.

   c) A good friend of a patient who has been admitted to a psychiatric unit demands to know why her friend has been admitted.

   d) An insurance company rings you to ask about the diagnosis of a patient who has recently taken out a large life insurance policy.

5. A Moslem man is admitted to your residential home. He was recently discharged from hospital after treatment for a stomach complaint where he lost a lot of weight. He needs a healthy diet, but it is Ramadan and he refuses to eat between sunrise and sunset. What would you do?

   a) Insist that he eats his special diet at the same time as the other residents.

   b) Accept his fasting, offering him a slice of toast and a cup of tea for his supper.

   c) Allow his family to leave food for you to warm up for him at the times when he is allowed to eat.

   d) Insist that he goes home if he is not willing to follow the routines of the nursing home.

6. Which of the following strategies is usually not appropriate for dealing with challenging behaviour?

   a) Getting conflicting parties to negotiate a settlement they can all live with

   b) Reprimanding a person for being abusive or aggressive

   c) Getting the conflicting parties to start work

   d) Providing feedback to people about the effects of their challenging behaviour on others

7. One of the people in your care makes a complaint that a fellow resident is continually threatening him with violence. What would you do?

   a) Make an immediate written record of the details of the complaint.

   b) Write up the complaint in the care record at the end of the shift.

   c) Ignore the complaint in the hope that the situation will "cool down" over the next couple of days.

   d) Mention the problem to the person-in-charge, when she arrives on duty in four hours time.

8. Which of the following strategies is not appropriate for a person who is at slight risk of minor physical abuse.

   a) Report signs and symptoms of abuse immediately to the person-in-charge.

   b) Ensure that the care plan outlines in detail the level of supervision that is required.

   c) Keep the person under constant supervision until there is no longer a risk.

   d) Report any significant changes in the person's physical or mental condition.

Module 2

Using Communication and Interpersonal Skills

Use your communication skills to help others.

Need-to-know words:

- aphasia
- articulation
- communication
- crisis
- empathy
- interpersonal skills
- mental defence mechanism
- modulation
- non-verbal communication
- rapport
- stress
- stroke
- therapeutic relationship
- unconditional positive regard

Objectives:

- Describe good communication skills.
- Identify common communication problems.
- Outline how to challenge another person's behaviour.
- Highlight barriers to communication.
- Outline how to assess communication differences.
- Assist individuals to communicate.
- Describe strategies for managing stress.
- Outline how to provide help during a crisis.
- Describe the phases of a therapeutic relationship.
- Outline the skills of client-centred counselling.

Module 2 Introduction

Module 2 relates directly to three units of the level 3 NVQ/SVQ Award in Care:

Unit C1: **Promote effective communication and relationships** is a mandatory group A unit. It consists of two elements of competence:

- CL1.1 Develop relationships with people which value them as individuals

- CL1.2 Establish and maintain effective communication with people

Unit C2: **Promote communication with individuals where there are communication differences** is an option group B unit. It consists of two elements of competence:

- CL2.1 Determine the nature and scope of communication differences

- CL2.2 Contribute to effective communication where there are communication differences

Unit Z8: **Support individuals when they are distressed** is also an option group B unit. It consists of two elements of competence:

- Z8.1 Contribute to the prevention of client distress

- Z8.2 Support the client in times of distress

Part 1: Developing Relationships (CL1)

Everything you do or say communicates a message.

The ability to communicate well builds good working relationships with the people in your care and within the care team. The way you speak and listen sends messages to anyone who is listening or observing. Communication can positively or adversely affect everything you do in your work role.

It is important that verbal and non-verbal communications agree in order to send clear messages. Problems arise because most people are not aware of their non-verbal behaviour. If a person's verbal and non-verbal communications do not agree, the listener gets a mixed message. When messages are mixed, the non-verbal communication is often perceived with more clarity by the listener. For example, if you try to express concern while looking in another direction, you communicate that you are not interested.

Communication occurs in many forms. Verbal aspects of communication form an essential part of everyday life. However, people tend to have different abilities in terms of being able to interpret non-verbal aspects of communication.

	Vocal	Non-vocal
Verbal	Spoken word, e.g., speech, radio, television	Written word or symbol e.g., book, magazine, fax, e-mail
Non-verbal	Verbal mannerisms, e.g., sighs, stammer; vocal qualities (loudness, pitch; tone of voice)	Movement, facial expression, gestures, appearance, distance between speakers, etc.

Four Main Categories of Communication

To recognise the information people are trying to convey, you must try to interpret both the verbal and non-verbal aspects of a communication. The diagram above shows four forms of communication.

The goals of communication are:

- To ensure that a clear message is communicated and/or received

- To understand others and, in turn, be understood

- To get acceptance

- To achieve effective action

Exercise 2.1 🖊

Just as a written sentence has a beginning (capital letter), a middle, and an end (full stop), all interactions between two or more people also have a form of beginning (e.g., eye contact is achieved), middle (e.g., maintaining eye contact), and end (e.g., one party breaks eye contact and walks away). People and cultures have different ways or preferences for communicating the start, middle, and end of interactions.

When communicating with another person, the interaction provides information about that person. Following are examples:

- Ability to communicate clearly

- Level of understanding of the issues being discussed

- Self-image that is being projected

- Mood of the person

- Aspects of personality

- Accent may indicate social class, ethnicity, or place of birth

Misinterpretation of the signals, together with prejudices, can result in your assessment of the person being very wrong. Therefore, you often need to check your initial assessment by asking the person pertinent questions (e.g., "Are you feeling anxious today, Mr. Jones?").

Exercise 2.2 🖊

Communication generally follows culturally set rules. Most people learn the rules without being conscious of them, in the same way they do not have to think about how to walk. During good quality communication, a person plays the role of speaker and listener.

- **Good listeners** hear and concentrate, are attentive, and check that they understand what the speaker said.

- **Good speakers** use clear and concise vocabulary, provide openings (opportunities for the listener to join the conversation); use appropriate tone, pitch, and volume of voice; and use appropriate gestures and facial expressions.

Exercise 2.3 🖊

Verbal communications are only part of the message that you are trying to convey. To prevent mistakes, follow these guidelines:

- Use appropriate language when communicating with people in your care.

- Use an interpreter if you do not speak a common language. (Be aware of the impact that a third person may have on willingness to disclose and on confidentiality.)

- Communicate with people at their level of understanding. (Use an appropriate manner, level, and pace, according to individual abilities.)

- Speak slowly, repeating yourself where necessary.

- Modify your communication, if necessary, to get the message across.

- Do not shout at people who are having difficulty understanding you.

- Do not use medical jargon or long words which may be confusing.

Exercise 2.4 🖊

Non-verbal communication is at least as important as the words you use in face-to-face interaction. Non-verbal behaviour has the following functions:

- It replaces some speech.

- It complements the spoken word and/or reinforces what is said.

- It regulates the flow of communication between speaker and listener.

- It provides feedback to the other person, thus sustaining a conversation.

- It defines relationships between speaker and listener and acceptable patterns of behaviour.

Many messages are conveyed by non-verbal communication. By your non-verbal actions, people can interpret whether you are happy or sad, feel dominant or subordinate, friendly or angry. Non-verbal behaviour varies from person to person and between cultures. Actions that are commonplace for some may be totally unacceptable to others.

- **Touch** is less common for British people when communicating compared to the Continentals. The places of the body that you touch are bound by social rules. For example, guiding another person's movements by steering at the elbow is acceptable; putting your hand on a man's or woman's knee or thigh while talking may be highly unacceptable.

- **Gaze** often starts an interaction. The person listening gives more eye contact than the person talking. Too much eye contact or staring creates anxiety.

- **Hand movements** are mainly used as illustrators and emphasisers. Be aware of cultural differences. (For example, the A-OK signal made by joining the thumb and forefinger into a circle, in France, means that you are worth zero. In Italy, it describes somebody as an "asshole.") Hand movements can also replace speech (e.g., Makaton or sign language).

- **Facial expression** is closely observed during interaction as it modifies everything that is said or done by showing emotions, providing feedback, indicating attitude, etc.

- **Posture** is very important in communicating attitudes and feelings. For example, at the start of an informal interview, it is important to sit straight, facing the person, leaning slightly forward to indicate interest. Talk to people at the same physical level, whenever possible; standing over them can be intimidating.

- **Distance** often indicates the relationship between two people. Spouses, lovers, and children are usually allowed within 18 inches—the "intimate" space. From 18 inches to four feet is "personal" space for friends, and four to nine feet is "social" space for most relationships. Personal space varies; what invades the personal space of one person will not do so for another.

Exercise 2.5 🖉

Listening

There are two types of listening. **Passive** listening involves the absorption of information, but the listener need not interact with the speaker (e.g., spies, eaves droppers). **Active** listening is also the absorption of information, but, there is also an obvious interaction.

The active listener listens with all the senses and signals either verbally or non-verbally that the message is understood and encourages the speaker to continue.

Verbally signal active listening:

- Provide acknowledgement and confirmation of the other person (e.g., say "Yes," "Right," "Okay," "Mm-hmm," or make appropriate sounds where the intonation of the sounds determines the nature of the response).

- Reflect back to the person your interpretation of what was said.

- Provide appropriate praise, encouragement, and support to signal involvement on the part of the listener. The interest must appear sincere, rather than patronising.

- Appropriately interrupt or disagree to stimulate interaction (not in a way that communicates that you think what you have to say is more important).

Non-verbally signal active listening:

- Indicate with the head (e.g., nods) and facial expressions (e.g., smiles, frowns).
- Use appropriate eye contact.
- Mirror similar facial expressions and body position.
- Adopt an attentive posture.

Exercise 2.6

General Barriers to Communication

Barriers to communication affect relationships and interfere with interaction. Avoid the following barriers:

- Appearing bored or impatient
- Threatening others or using harsh language
- Negating, devaluing, or being critical of others
- Jumping to conclusions
- Passing judgment or giving unwanted advice
- Arguing or interrupting

- Distracting (e.g., fiddling or doodling)
- Confusing people with multiple questions
- Mumbling or confused presentation
- Having physical barriers between you and the client (e.g., a desk)
- Being in environments that are distracting or uncomfortable

Enhancing Relationships

Good relationships are the foundation of a comfortable working experience. Treating people with respect and dignity builds good relationships.

- **Always knock** before entering a person's room. Remember that this is an individual's living quarters. Provide the privacy and courtesy you would show to people in their own homes.

- **Introduce yourself.** Some people have difficulty remembering names. Say your name whenever you enter a person's room to avoid confusion or embarrassment.

- **Ask how a person wishes to be addressed.** Some people prefer not to be called by their first names.

- **Provide comfort.** Pay attention to a person's needs.

- **Support individual rights and choices** within the limits of your work role. Encourage individuals to express their wishes and needs.

- **Be courteous and respectful of visitors.** Family and friends influence the well-being of clients. Provide privacy if desired. If you must provide care, politely ask visitors to leave the room, and let them know when they can return.

- **Maintain privacy and dignity at all times.** Everyone wants to be loved and have friends with shared interests. Regardless of age, people are sexual beings with sexual desires. Deal with sexuality in a mature, professional manner. Allow privacy, and do not interfere with consenting partners as long as the individuals concerned are not likely to come to any harm. If problems arise, ask your manager how to handle the situation.

Exercise 2.7 🖉

Challenging Unacceptable Behaviour

Remember that different people behave differently and can have very different views on the acceptability of behaviour. This will depend on a person's attitude and values which have been moulded by upbringing and life experiences. One person's appropriate and acceptable behaviour may be unreasonable and offensive to another person (e.g., somebody is offended by another person's rude or warped sense of humour).

The crux of the matter comes when you feel that someone has overstepped the mark of acceptable behaviour. In some cases, it is appropriate to challenge the person (e.g., when somebody makes repeated sexist remarks to you or when someone's behaviour is upsetting the people in your care). The challenge can take the form of a gentle reminder of more appropriate ways to behave, or you may need to be assertive in your challenge.

At other times, you can appropriately laugh off or ignore another person's undesirable behaviour (e.g., when someone accidentally spills a drink and swears). Remember to take into account the cultural norms for the situation, and try to balance them against your personal beliefs.

Exercise 2.8 🖉

The following examples are assertive ways that you can choose to challenge another person's behaviour:

- Say, "I find swearing offensive; please do not swear in front of me again."
- Remind the person that the behaviour is upsetting and/or offending other people.
- Inform the person that the behaviour is illegal (e.g., racist, sexist, or likely to cause a breach of the peace) and that you will have to inform your manager/the police if the behaviour does not stop.

You have to choose the correct time and place to challenge another person's behaviour, or you may make the situation worse. The person may not be able to stop behaving this way (e.g., due to mental illness, epilepsy, senile dementia, intoxication). In these situations, choosing ways other than directly challenging the person are usually more effective at managing the situation.

Part 2: Overcoming Communication Differences (CL2)

Promote communication for people who have communication difficulties.

The model on the right explains differences in the way that people communicate. Messages are taken in by the body's senses (e.g., sight, hearing, touch, and smell). These are then decoded so that the person can interpret an initial meaning. In turn, they are transferred to other parts of the brain where they are linked with a person's ideas, feelings, values, and attitudes so that the message is fully understood.

When messages are to be sent out, a person's ideas, feelings, values, and attitude affect that person's intention and eventual behaviour selection. This is encoded into a message that is suitable for transmission before the message is given out by the person (via a variety of modes of communication—verbal and non-verbal).

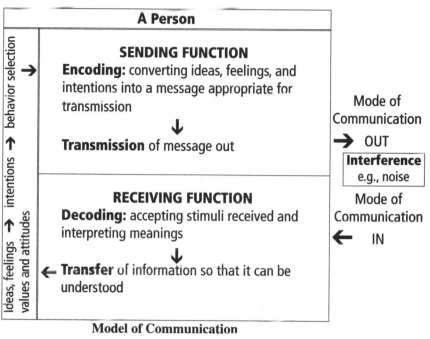

Model of Communication

Most aspects of taking in and sending out messages are automatic; that is, you do not have to think about it to be able to do it. It takes energy to actively listen for messages and concentrate on giving out a correct message. To communicate effectively, the following four things are necessary:

- Normal physical and psychological development through childhood to the present time
- Good physical and mental health
- A minimum of communication interference in the environment
- A common language

Exercise 2.9 🖉

Specific Barriers to Communication

People vary in intelligence, education, religion, culture, social background, and experience. These differences create very different frames of reference where each person sees the world in a different and unique way.

All the areas outlined in the communication model can be the focus for barriers to communication. Specific barriers to communication are outlined below.

Environmental Interference:

- Noise may make it difficult to hear and be heard.
- Distractions may include bright sunlight, several people speaking at once, smells, dress, and appearance of others.
- Level of comfort may include too hot or cold, discomfort (e.g., shoes rubbing).
- Lack of privacy.

Decoding Barriers:

- Sensory problems (e.g., poor sight or hearing)
- Language used and accent (e.g., Geordie, French, sign language)
- Terminology and unfamiliar words
- Level of attention and any preoccupations (e.g., with catching the train home)
- Length of communication and memory
- Ability to discriminate

Comprehension Barriers:

- Mental health problems (e.g., thought blocking)
- Low intelligence (i.e., inability to comprehend)
- Level of knowledge about the subject area being discussed
- Attitude and values, stereotypes, and prejudices
- Level of anxiety and worry
- Mental defence mechanisms
- Strong emotions
- Verbal and non-verbal messages not matching

Encoding Barriers:

- Mental health problems (i.e., confusion and disorientation)
- Low intelligence
- Concentrating on yourself (i.e., deciding that you are going to get your message across, no matter what)
- Level of knowledge about the subject area being discussed
- Attitudes and values, stereotypes, and prejudices
- Level of anxiety and worry
- Strong emotions
- Unwilling to communicate or tell the truth

Transmission Barriers:

- Physical problems (e.g., limb paralysis, inability to articulate properly, sore throat)
- Language and accent used (e.g., French, sign language)
- Terminology and unfamiliar words
- Level of attention and any preoccupations (e.g., anxious in case you make a mistake)
- Length of communication and memory

Exercise 2.10 🖉

Ensure that other professionals are used, where appropriate, to assess communication problems and overcome communication differences (e.g., speech therapist, interpreter, psychologist).

Whatever the barrier to communication, it can interfere with the provision of quality care. The following examples can be the result of poor communication:

- Non-compliance with the requests of care staff
- Misunderstandings that lead to lack of trust
- Distress caused by not being able to communicate well
- Reduction in a person's self-esteem
- Difficulty in assessing other problems
- Confusion leading to mistakes being made
- Anger, depression, and feelings of helplessness when care needs are not being met

Assessing Communication Differences

To accurately assess communication problems, there is a need to develop a rapport. The best way to build a rapport is by generating empathy with the other person. This involves listening to what the other person has to say and, more importantly, watching the person's response. While a person may say how he or she is feeling, non-verbal communication provides clues to how the person is really feeling.

Assessing communication problems can be difficult because of the time needed to carry out an accurate assessment. Carers often have many people that require their care, limiting the amount of time that can be spent with one person. The time is further limited by other activities (e.g., the need to keep accurate records, answering the telephone).

It is often appropriate to seek further information about a person's communication abilities by approaching other sources (e.g., family, friends, other professionals). This can help to determine the correct method of communication to use. Sometimes a person is known to have good communication skills, but simply chooses not to use them. Or the situation may prevent the person from using good communication skills.

Communication skills are usually assessed in more detail after a communication problem has been identified by the care staff. Detailed assessments are usually carried out by a speech therapist. The only time communication skills assessments are carried out by care staff is when they are part of a larger assessment of a person's general abilities or level of development. (Examples include Portage checklist for the assessment of a child's level of development, and Progress Assessment Chart for the assessment of the abilities of people who have learning disabilities.)

Exercise 2.11

Assisting Individuals to Communicate

Before planning commences, the level and type of assistance needed by the individual should be established by assessment. Care strategies should be appropriate to the person's level of understanding and preferred mode of communication. The carer should try to use both verbal and non-verbal skills, as appropriate, that are consistent with the person's own expression and use. Preferably, different methods of overcoming the communication problem should be identified in the care plan. Aids to communication should be made available where appropriate (e.g., notepad and pencil, computer, flashcards).

The communication used by care staff should be consistent with the plan of care and delivered at an appropriate pace and level of understanding. Create opportunities for the person to communicate (e.g., during leisure activities and while care is being provided). Encourage, stimulate, and interest the person in order to promote communication. Remember that a person's communication abilities may not be indicative of the person's level of understanding.

When the plan of care includes recording of the person's communication skills, be clear, concise, and objective. Be aware of the times when the person, appropriately, may not want to communicate. Be aware of and sensitive to any conflicts between the care plan and the person's choice of communication. (For example, the plan of care might be to stimulate the person to speak, but the person might be too embarrassed to demonstrate a speech impediment.)

Be aware that there are many different ways to overcome communication difficulties and differences. Following are examples:

- Identify yourself when entering the room, and explain what you are going to do.

- Be clear about what you want to say, and choose an appropriate time.

- Be patient.

- Carefully choose the location, and provide privacy as needed.

- Use communication aids (e.g., pictures, paper and pencil).

35

- Ensure that the person can clearly see your face, especially if he or she reads lips.

- Get close to the person who is partially deaf, and speak loudly enough to be heard without shouting (using the side where hearing is best).

- Eliminate unnecessary noises (e.g., TV, radio).

- Address the person by name.

- Speak slowly; use simple words and appropriate language.

- Make the message clear, without too many details.

- Take time to check that the person understands you.

- Allow time for the person to respond.

- Use "touch" as appropriate.

- Modify a message so that it can be understood (e.g., giving examples, providing an analogy, using pictures, emphasizing facial expressions and tone of voice).

- Be supportive and positive.

- Remember that concepts are often difficult to translate into other languages (including sign language).

- Talk normally; do not "talk down" to the person nor shout.

- Ask the person to repeat if necessary, rather than pretending to understand.

- If the person uses a hearing aid, make sure that it is being worn and that it is clean.

- Use gestures when appropriate.

- Remind anyone who needs spectacles to wear them, and offer to clean the spectacles if necessary.

Various methods of communication are available to support individuals who have communication difficulties (e.g., Makaton, Deaf Sign Language, Amerind).

Exercise 2.12 🖉

Part 3: Supporting People in Distress (Z8)

People need your support when they are distressed.

Stress is an unpleasant emotional experience associated with elements of fear, dread, anxiety, irritation, anger, sadness, and grief. Stress is unavoidable. When individuals cannot cope with the stress in their lives, they are referred to as being distressed. Therefore, a person's ability to cope with stress is an important factor in preventing distress from occurring.

Before you can help other people cope with their stress, it is important that you understand the different components of stress. Each of the four components

highlighted in the model below is an area in the stress process where intervention can be focused.

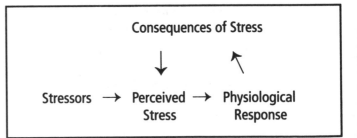

Model for Understanding Stress

Stressors are physical and/or emotional demands made on a person by his or her environment. There are two main types of stressors. *Major stressors* are severe stressors or intense pressures (e.g., death in the family, divorce, redundancy). *Minor stressors* are small problems that occur during a normal day, often referred to as hassles (e.g., disappointments, traffic jams). Most minor stressors can be easily coped with, but the cumulative effect of repeated exposure can be highly stressful.

Exercise 2.13 🖎

A person's **perception of a stressor** is the key to understanding why people can respond very differently to the same stressor. The two main components of perceived stress are the person and the situation. Personal factors include values, attitudes, personal goals, and personality. Situational factors include duration of the stressor, perceived level of control over the stressor, and available social support.

The **physiological response** starts with the brain perceiving a stressor that is strong enough to stimulate the sympathetic nervous system to release adrenaline into the blood stream. If the stressor is strong enough, the level of adrenaline causes the characteristic "fight or flight" response, which is essential for personal survival. Usually stressors stimulate the release of lower levels of adrenaline.

Adrenaline prepares the body for action by making the heart beat faster and sending a greater proportion of blood to the brain and muscles. Increasing levels of stress can improve a person's performance, but only until the optimum level of arousal has been reached. Beyond this point, performance deteriorates as increasing levels of stress are experienced. When stressors occur over a long period of time, the body becomes worn out by having to deal with the increased levels of adrenaline.

The **consequences of stress** fall into five categories:

- Effects on health: There is an unusually high risk of developing a physical illness (e.g., high blood pressure, stomach ulcers, insomnia) for people who have high stress occupations and people who experience major stressors.

- Psychological effects: Emotions intensify (e.g., anger, helplessness, guilt), and ability to cope decreases. There may be an inability to think clearly (e.g., in problem solving, use of mental defence mechanisms). Watch for signals which might indicate that more complicated emotions are surfacing (e.g., aggression, suicidal tendencies).

- Behavioural consequences: There can be over-reaction (e.g., increased expressions of mistrust, pettiness, anger) or overindulgence (e.g., increased consumption of tobacco, caffeine, food, alcohol, drugs) used as a crutch to "get through the day."

- Occupational consequences: There can be a general lowering of efficiency and effectiveness at work, with increased errors and reduced productivity.

- Social consequences: There can be difficulty maintaining relationships or a lack of energy to enjoy life.

Exercise 2.14 🖎

Managing Stress

Strategies for managing stress use the main components identified in the model as the focus. Not all of the strategies will be appropriate for all people in all situations. The aim is to find the right blend of coping strategies to help each individual cope with stress.

Coping with Stressors: Although stress is unavoidable, it is sometimes possible to eliminate, reduce, or avoid stressors. For example, the stress of traffic jams and finding parking spaces can be avoided by taking the train. The stress related to a care environment can be escaped by opting for home treatment. Unfortunately, some stressors cannot be avoided (e.g., death of a relative).

Coping with perceived stress: To cope with perceived stress, self-awareness is important. The aim is to achieve an understanding and acceptance of self. When this has occurred, a person is ready to deal with stress. One useful way of coping with perceived stress is to think about the stressful situation in more positive terms. For example, being made redundant could be viewed as an opportunity to start a new, more worthwhile career.

Coping with the physiological response: If the body is slowly wearing out due to increased levels of adrenaline in the blood, you need to reduce the level of adrenaline that is released by the sympathetic nervous system. This is done by stimulating the parasympathetic nervous system. Two main ways of triggering the parasympathetics are *physical exercise* and *relaxation.* Physical exercise triggers the system directly. The exercise should be enjoyable, rather than competitive and overdone. Relaxation triggers the system indirectly via the use of relaxation techniques, meditation, deep breathing, massage, etc.

The following strategies can be used to cope with the consequences of stress:

- Exercise and healthy eating help to burn off adrenaline and prevent the build up of cholesterol in the arteries.

- Creative use of leisure time, including physical and mental activities, helps take the mind off problems.

- Good interpersonal relationships with friends and family can help a person to talk through problems and receive appropriate support.

Exercise 2.15

Supporting People in Crisis

Crisis refers to a turning point or a decisive moment when a person is faced with an urgent, stressful situation which feels overwhelming (Parry, 1990). A crisis includes the following essential features:

- **Stress event** (e.g., death of a spouse, any long-term stressor, severe financial problems)

- **Distress** (e.g., a stressor that is perceived as being overwhelming)

- **Loss, danger, or humiliation** (e.g., loss of a career when made redundant, humiliation when caught shoplifting)

- **Inability to control** the situation

- **Unexpected event** (e.g., a woman who has just discovered her husband is having an affair)

- **Disruption of routine** (e.g., being made redundant means not having to go to work)

- **Uncertainty** about the future (e.g., your home has been repossessed and not knowing where you are going to be living)

- **Distress that occurs over time** (typically two to six weeks)

Situations which trigger a crisis may seem quite trivial, but the event may be "the straw that breaks the camel's back." The apparently trivial cause of the crisis can result in others deciding that the level of distress is inappropriate for the situation, and the person can be unfairly labelled as "mentally frail" or "pathetic."

Exercise 2.16

A person's response to crisis can include any of the consequences of stress. In addition, there are various other feelings that people often experience:

- Not real: a short-term feeling that the situation is not real and that the person will waken from a dream

- Anaesthesia: a short-term feeling of numbness caused by shock which results from the release of chemicals in the body that protect a person from pain

- Avoidance or pre-occupation: with the problem

- Anger, shame and guilt: regarding the problem

Some people feel so depressed that they want to harm themselves. These people are usually kept under close observation, whenever possible. Make sure you know your organisation's policies on managing people who want to harm themselves. It is important that you do not become too involved and know when to ask for help when dealing with people in crisis.

Coping with a crisis can be very difficult, especially when there is an inability to think clearly and solve problems. It is important to assess the help that a person needs during a crisis. The required help can usually be placed into one of four categories—emotional support, information and advice, companionship, or practical help (Parry, 1990).

- Emotional support: Be there for the person, to provide physical contact and a safe environment in which to express emotions.

- Information: Provide information and advice (e.g., "You might want to consider a visit to the Citizens Advice Bureau where they'll understand what you're going through").

- Companionship: The social network is important in re-establishing a grip on reality. Contact with other people ensures that there is somebody with whom the person can talk or spend time and take his or her mind off the problems.

- Practical help: Provide help with simple tasks such as washing, ironing, or shopping.

If the crisis appears to be escalating despite your best efforts, inform your manager at the earliest opportunity, before the situation gets out of hand.

Exercise 2.17

Death and Bereavement

Death and bereavement are important crises which affect almost everyone at some point in life. You may have to care for people who are dying. Do not allow your fear of death to stop you from being sensitive to the needs of the dying person and the family.

Caring for Someone who is Dying

Follow these guidelines when providing care for someone who is dying.

- Make the person as comfortable as possible.

- Continue normal care.

- Encourage the person to suggest how he or she could best be supported. This might include not leaving the person alone or keeping the room well-lit if darkness is frightening.

- Talk in a normal voice.

- Do not tiptoe.

- Provide comfort and support for the person and the family as required.

- Respect the need for time and privacy with close family and friends.

- Provide spiritual support if requested.

- Allow the person to die with dignity.

Exercise 2.18 🖉

Stages of Grief

People who believe they are about to die react in different ways. Moods may change from day to day as they grieve over life ending. Family members often experience the same feelings. In her work with dying patients, Elizabeth Kubler-Ross (1969) identified five stages of grief—denial, anger, depression, bargaining, and acceptance. The stages apply to any major loss. Not everyone goes through all five stages, nor is there a specific order. Some may repeat stages. Being familiar with the five stages of grief will help you to understand what the person and the family are experiencing.

Denial is a state of shock when the person cannot accept what is happening. The person may insist it is a mistake or may ignore the facts completely.

- Do not force the person to face the truth.
- Give the person time to adjust.
- Listen when he or she wants to talk.
- Do not force conversation.

Anger is normal. People express anger at God, at the doctor, at life, perhaps even at you. They may yell at you, accuse you of poor care, complain about everything, or refuse to do anything you ask.

- Be patient.
- Continue giving the best care you can.
- Do not take insults personally.
- Do not become defensive.

Depression happens when people have partially accepted death. People become discouraged and sad. They are sorting out their feelings. Sometimes people become very withdrawn and may not want to eat or socialise. Others become more talkative and need more of your time.

- Being there for the person is very important. If he or she wants to talk, listen patiently.
- Be compassionate. If the person does not want to talk, do not force conversation.
- Give the best care possible.

Bargaining is when people try to make deals to postpone death. They will bargain with God or the doctors. Sometimes they may try to bargain with you.

- Listen with a caring attitude.
- Never make promises or say, "Things will be alright."
- Let the person know you are there for them.
- Hold the person's hand for comfort.

Acceptance is when the person accepts that death is inevitable. It does not mean that he or she wants to die. The person may be talkative or may be very quiet. Spending time with close relatives or friends can be very comforting for the person.

- Be there to hold a hand and keep the person from feeling alone.
- Continue routine care.
- Provide privacy with loved ones.
- If a member of clergy is requested, let the person-in-charge know immediately.

Exercise 2.19 🖉

Therapeutic Relationships

A therapeutic relationship refers to a long-term relationship between a carer and a person receiving care. Therapeutic relationships can be very stressful because working closely with people who are highly stressed is very demanding. The relationship does not happen automatically; it is achieved through hard work.

Three phases of a therapeutic relationship have been identified by Ironbar and Hooper (1989)—introductory, working, and termination.

Introductory Phase: On meeting, both parties tend to appraise each other, forming their initial impressions. The carer needs to demonstrate confidence (by appropriate verbal and nonverbal communication and showing competence in the job), and warmth (by showing genuine concern, personal recognition, respect, and support for the other person).

Working Phase: The quality of the relationship directly affects how effective the carer can be in helping the person work through personal problems, maintain individuality, and learn from the experience. The carer uses counselling skills to develop the relationship. The most important aspect of this phase is to develop empathy. You need to accurately perceive the feelings of the other person and understand what that person is trying to communicate to you (Tschudin, 1989). This provides the foundation for planning the way ahead.

Termination Phase: Eventually, the relationship with the carer will have to end. Use this experience positively as the person regains autonomy and personal control over his or her own life.

Exercise 2.20

Counselling

Listening is an important communication skill used within counselling. You can provide help and support by being an understanding listener. Create a climate in which the person needing help feels accepted and confident enough to be able to talk freely about thoughts and feelings, without having to be defensive. As a result of being able to talk freely, a person can gain greater insight into the problem and be able to resolve the problem or cope better with the situation.

The counsellor does not offer ready-made solutions or answers. The counsellor encourages the client to think things through and work out his or her own solutions to problems. There are often strong emotions felt by the client that the counsellor has to manage. Before you take on any formal counselling, it is important that you receive relevant training and achieve a qualification in counselling skills.

Non-directive, client-centred counselling has certain pre-requisites that the counsellor has to offer before successful counselling can take place (Brearley & Birchley, 1986).

- Empathy: The counsellor, without making pre-judgments, attempts to perceive the world

as the client perceives it and conveys this understanding to the client, mainly by reflection.

- Congruence: The counsellor recognises his or her personal feelings so that they are not allowed to impinge on the relationship (e.g., when talking about a subject that is causing difficulties in the counsellor's own life).

- Non-possessive warmth: The counsellor expresses a warm, unconditional concern for the client, whatever his or her cultural, racial, religious, social or political background.

If a counsellor cannot offer these pre-requisites to any client who requires counselling, then the counsellor should hand over the client to someone else for counselling who can be non-directive and client-centred. People are products of their upbringing and life experiences. Everybody has some prejudices against certain groups of people. If you have a strong prejudice, you cannot be non-judgmental; therefore, you should not try to counsel these people.

Exercise 2.21

Be alert to the different ways that you can support someone who needs help. Listed below are five types of counselling.

- Developmental: helps people confront and deal with specific developmental tasks in their lives. The main emphasis is on development of the person, rather than on specific problems or decisions (e.g., promoting self-awareness).

- Problem-focused: helps people overcome or learn to cope better with one or more specific problems (e.g., marital disharmony)

- Decision-making: helps people to make specific decisions (e.g., choosing a career)

- Crisis intervention: helps people who feel overwhelmed and are having difficulty coping. The people are often highly emotional, and the counsellor simply works towards getting them over the worst of the crisis (e.g., redundancy)

- Support: helps people who are not going through a crisis, but who need extra support to help them through awkward phases in their lives

You should be clear about the different roles of a trained counsellor who undertakes formal counselling sessions and your supporting role in using your counselling skills when providing care. If you feel that a client needs counselling, do not wait; notify the person-in-charge.

Exercise 2.22

Counselling involves the use of a wide range of relationship and communication skills. Put the client at ease with a welcome and smiling acknowledgement. Reassure the client about the boundaries of confidentiality (e.g., the information will only be discussed with other members of the care team, if they need to know), and demonstrate active listening.

Use the following *verbal* interventions that encourage the client to talk:

- Restate: Repeat the ideas of the client in your own words.

- Reflect: Accurately identify and reflect back the client's own feelings.

- Summarise: Give a brief outline, simply and clearly, of the main issues outlined by the client.

- Paraphrase: Use your own words to rephrase the essential meaning of what the client is saying.

- Focus on specific issues that need to be explored further.

- Ask open questions (e.g., "How?" or "What if...?"), rather than closed questions requiring one word answers.

- Negotiate for meaning when a person's words do not seem to carry the intended message (e.g., "What I think you mean is...").

Use the following *non-verbal* guidelines:

- Maintain an attentive and open body posture (e.g., uncrossed legs, unfolded arms, lean slightly forward to show interest, use appropriate eye contact).

- Choose appropriate seating arrangements (e.g., do not sit behind a desk, ensure that chairs are at a slight angle to each other).

- Reflect the person's facial expressions, and provide affirmative head nodding.

Barriers to Counselling

Avoid the following barriers to counselling:

- Being judgmental: jumping to conclusions, communicating to the client that to be accepted, he or she must think as you think

- Making reassuring statements: trying to do magic with words (e.g., saying "Everything will be fine")

- Giving advice: seen as different from supplying the client with information

- Changing topics: including interrupting. (usually used to protect the counsellor from having to broach stressful topics)

- Showing indifference: fiddling, mumbling, assuming a condescending attitude, or making rejecting statements

Exercise 2.23

Summary

Everything you do and say communicates a message, and the ability to communicate well builds good relationships. Choose your words carefully, and reflect a caring attitude with your listening skills, facial expressions, gestures, posture, etc. As a carer, you need to deal effectively with unacceptable behaviour and to overcome communication differences. Understanding stress helps you to prevent and manage stress in the care environment and to support clients in times of distress.

Check Your Knowledge and Understanding

1. Which of the following are communication problems?

    a) A person speaks a foreign language that you do not understand.

    b) A person is not telling the truth.

    c) A person has misinterpreted what you have said.

    d) A person is distressed and angry.

2. A person in your care is a little confused. She is to be discharged home this afternoon. She needs to know about her medication that has been prescribed for her to take home. She also needs to know about the place that has been organised for her at a day centre. What would you do?

    a) Inform the lady about her discharge plan, and hope that she understands and remembers the information.

    b) Inform the lady, and then write down the information on a sheet of paper for her to keep as a reminder.

    c) Do not inform the lady; inform the relative who will soon arrive to take her home.

    d) Inform both the lady and the relative, and provide them with the sheet of paper with all the details.

3. You are counselling a young man who has personal problems. He says that he would like to explore the effect that the death of his mother has had on him. Your father has been very ill for the past fortnight and you are afraid he might die. You are not sure whether you can cope with talking about this sensitive subject area. What should you do?

    a) Stop the counselling session, and refer the young man to another counsellor.

    b) Ask him not to talk about that subject.

    c) Direct him to talk about something different.

    d) Continue with the counselling session, and just cope with your feelings.

4. In planning care to overcome a communication difference or problem, which of the following is incorrect?

    a) A full assessment of the communication problem should be carried out before the care is planned.

    b) The person should be asked to speak plain English.

    c) You should try to encourage a distressed person, who is not yet ready to talk, to discuss potential answers to his personal problems.

    d) Preferably, different methods for overcoming the communication problem should be identified in the care plan.

5. One of your residents in a care home insists on telling crude jokes and attempts to pinch the bottoms of carers whenever he gets the opportunity. His behaviour is making some of the carers avoid him, and he is upsetting some of the other residents. What should you do?

   a) Reprimand the resident, informing him that he will be asked to leave if he mis-behaves again.

   b) Ignore his behaviour in the hope that it will stop.

   c) Move him to a side ward where the other residents will not be bothered by his behaviour. Leave a note in the office reminding carers not to bend down in front of him.

   d) Have a quiet word with him. Describe the effects of his sexual assaults and jokes on the carers and the other resi-dents. Negotiate with him to stop pinching bottoms and to "tone down" his jokes.

6. A friend confides to you that his boss is causing him a lot of stress at work, and recently he has started getting palpitations before going into meetings where his boss is going to be present. What is the most appropriate advice to give to your friend?

   a) "Find another job."

   b) "Try learning relaxation techniques to use before each meeting with the boss."

   c) "Try to avoid going to the meetings."

   d) "Go to the pub for some 'Dutch courage' before the meetings."

Contributing to Health, Safety, and Security

Need-to-know words:

- acidosis
- angina
- antibody
- audit
- crepitus
- defibrillation
- disinfection
- hyperglycaemia
- hypoglycaemia
- ketones
- micro-organisms
- seizure
- sterilisation
- stroke
- tumour

People depend on you for a healthy, safe, and secure care environment.

Objectives:

- Explain the principles of client security.
- Outline the management of cash and valuables.
- Explain how to prevent accidents.
- Discuss relevant legislation covering health and safety.
- Discuss how to deal with environmental emergencies.
- Demonstrate safe manual handling.
- Utilise the principles of infection control.
- Demonstrate how to deal with health emergencies.

Module 3 Introduction

Module 3 relates to just one unit of the level 3 NVQ/SVQ Award in Care:

Unit CU1: **Promote, Monitor, and Maintain Health, Safety, and Security in the Workplace**. This is a mandatory group A unit that consists of three elements of competence:

- CU1.1   Monitor and maintain the safety and security of the work environment

- CU1.2   Promote standards of health and safety in working practice

- CU1.3   Minimise the risks arising from health emergencies

Part 1:   Maintaining Health, Safety, and Security   (CU1)

Simple precautions prevent serious injuries and maintain security.

A wide range of subject areas are covered within this unit—safety and security, health and safety at work, lifting and moving, infection control, and first aid.

There are three important reasons for the security of the people in your care—legal, clinical, and personal safety.

- **Legal reasons** (e.g., a child provided with a "place of safety," a person referred to a regional secure unit for assessment)

- **Clinical reasons** (e.g., a person who needs regular medication or treatment, a person with an infection who is isolated)

- **Personal safety reasons** (e.g., a person with a learning disability who might wander off and suffer from exposure, a person who may attempt to take his own life)

Establishments have different levels and methods of security. For example, a special hospital might lock all client rooms at night; use cameras, alarms and special lighting; or employ security staff to monitor entrances and exits. In contrast, a psychiatric hospital might only lock up a small area (such as a secure ward) and make regular checks for the presence of clients.

Whatever the level of security of the building, you need to be sure of your legal rights to prevent someone from leaving or entering.

Follow these guidelines:

- Establish rights of entry before allowing callers to enter premises. If you have an appointments system, stick to it unless there is good reason for not doing so.

- Carefully explain any restrictions on a person's freedom to the person involved, and ensure that all staff know about the restrictions.

- If a client who cannot be prevented from leaving is likely to wander off and be in danger, clearly state in the care plan the level and method of supervision for this person.

Missing Client

If a person goes missing, follow these steps:

- Search the building thoroughly.

- Search the grounds and local areas.

- Ask the staff and other clients to see if anyone knows where the person might have gone.

Exercise 3.1 🖉

If not found, the person-in-charge will have to set in motion the missing-person's procedure. This includes making a note of when the person was last seen, when it was noticed that the person was missing, what the person was wearing when last seen, and if there are any restrictions on freedom.

Police need to be contacted, especially, if the person is legally not allowed to leave the building or if the person is likely to be in any danger. The police will want the same details as above, plus they will want a description of the person. They will also want to know about any places or people that the missing person is likely to visit and whether the person is dangerous.

Ensure that all details concerning this incident are clearly written up in the person's care plan and on any forms that have to be completed.

Exercise 3.2

Safety of Money and Valuables

Encourage people to keep their personal belongings in secure and appropriate places. Discourage vulnerable people from keeping too much money or too many valuables on them. Ensure that you know and follow any policies or procedures for handling money or valuables.

Lock expensive equipment away when not in use. Keep equipment inventory up to date so that it is easy to check if something goes missing. Mark all expensive equipment by engraving and/or writing a security code in ultra-violet-sensitive ink. Secure buildings during the day and night as appropriate.

If valuables go missing or are stolen, the police will almost certainly be called in, and everybody will be under suspicion. Anyone found guilty of stealing will probably be dismissed.

If you have any concerns regarding health, safety, and security, seek advice from an appropriate person (e.g., health and safety officer, security officer, fire officer, the police).

Exercise 3.3

Ensuring Safe Environments

The Health and Safety at Work Act (1974) identifies responsibilities for the employer, the employee, and the management for ensuring a safe environment.

Employee duties include the following:

- Care for the health and safety of self and others.
- Comply with the requirements imposed on the employer.
- Adhere to instructions in the operation of plant and equipment.
- Use materials only according to recommended procedures.
- Use protective clothing and equipment, as directed.
- Never interfere or misuse anything provided for health, safety, and welfare.

Employer duties include the following:

- Ensure the health, safety, and welfare at work for all employees.
- Provide and maintain equipment and systems that are safe.
- Provide information, instruction, training, and supervision for health and safety at work.

Management responsibilities include the following:

- Maintain a safe environment for all staff.
- Ensure that staff adhere to health and safety orders, policies, and procedures.
- Provide training for safe practices and work methods.

- Explain hazards and safe practices to new employees before they commence work.
- Report and record all accidents.

Guidelines for care environments include the following:

- Maintain an environment of health, safety, and security based on allowing people who are receiving care to have individual choice in furnishings, activities, etc., that are consistent with organisational policies.

- Take appropriate action immediately whenever a person's health, safety, or security are threatened.

- Dress, behave, and practice personal hygiene in keeping with good health and safety practices, including the use of appropriate protection where necessary. Be a good role model for others.

- Record all accidents and incidents carefully and comprehensively in accordance with local and national policies, and keep your manager informed of events.

- If you have any concerns about health, safety, or security, seek advice from an appropriate person (e.g., your local health and safety representative).

Exercise 3.4

Control of Substances Hazardous to Health (COSHH) regulations require employers to assess the risks created at work where hazardous substances are used. This includes:

- The potential risks from using the substance in the place of work

- How the risks are to be managed

- What precautions should be taken in terms of storage, usage, disposal, etc.

The employer must provide training for all aspects of working with dangerous substances.

Exercise 3.5

Preventing Accidents

The best way to avoid an accident is to be alert to potential hazards by assessing the risk in any given situation. You have a duty to yourself, your family, your clients, and your colleagues to remain vigilant. If you notice a potential hazard, you may need to follow one or more of these general guidelines:

- Get out of harm's way.
- Remove, or make safe, the hazard, if possible.
- Inform an appropriate authority so that the hazard can be removed, replaced, or fixed.
- Label the hazard (e.g., "wet floors" sign).
- If appropriate, stay near the hazard so that you can keep others away.
- Inform everybody of the hazard at the earliest possibility.

Other simple strategies that you can take when entering "risk areas," include the following:

- Carefully preview the day's cases to check whether anybody who is in your care is potentially violent.

- Ask to have a colleague present, take an escort, or use a taxi, if unsure.

- Leave your itinerary and expected departure/arrival times.

- Tell colleagues, manager, etc., about possible changes to the plan.

- Arrange for contact if your return is overdue.

- Carry a personal alarm or portable telephone.

- Refrain from carrying a bag/briefcase or wearing an outer uniform or having car stickers that suggest you have money or drugs with you.

- Make sure you have an out-of-hours telephone number to summon help if needed.

Exercise 3.6 🖊

Falls are a significant cause of injury. The risk of falling is high for older people, usually due to general weakness, paralysis, confusion, dizziness, impaired vision, or other physical problems. Before making any changes to a person's immediate environment, ask the person for permission. This is a courtesy, as well as a safety factor.

Be alert to safety hazards and take extra precautions to protect elderly and frail people from injury. Simple precautions can prevent serious injuries.

- Remove obstacles to walking such as personal belongings, wires, or equipment.

- Wipe up spills immediately, taking into consideration the substance that has been spilled and the appropriate safe method for disposal.

- Assist people in and out of the bath as appropriate.

- Use good lighting.

- Use good wheelchair technique. Lock wheels when moving people to and from wheelchairs, and ensure that feet are securely placed on the foot rests when moving the wheelchair.

- Keep items that are used frequently close at hand so that the person does not fall reaching for them.

- Answer the call light promptly so that the person does not try to get up unaided. Do not leave helpless people unattended.

- Encourage people who are unsteady to use hand rails and other prescribed mobility aids when walking.

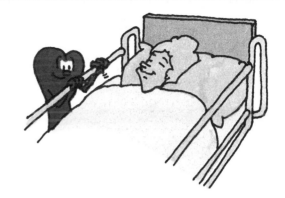

- Keep side rails up when the bed is occupied by someone who may fall out.

- Assist with walking if needed.

- Be alert to furniture or objects that pose a hazard.

Burns and scalds are preventable.

- Prevent fires and cigarette burns by enforcing no-smoking policies.

- Make sure bath water is not too hot. Test the water temperature yourself, and let the person who is having the bath test the water.

- Assist people, where appropriate, with hot foods and liquids.

Exercise 3.7 🖊

Accidental poisoning can be the result of carelessness, confusion, or not being able to read labels because of poor vision. Keep all cleaning agents and disinfectants locked in appropriate storage cupboards. Never place them in household food containers; they may be mistaken for food.

Choking can be prevented.

- Ensure clients are positioned properly for eating and swallowing.

- Supervise clients carefully at mealtimes if they are at risk of choking.

- Encourage clients to take smaller bites and to eat more slowly.

Prevent **electrocution:**

- Ensure that all electrical equipment that is brought into the care facility is checked by an electrician.

- Inspect all electrical equipment externally for obvious damage (e.g., frayed wires).

- Operate all equipment according to instructions. If in doubt, ask.

- Always ensure, where possible, that electrical equipment is properly earthed.

- Ensure that people and environments are dry before plugging in equipment.

- Do not overload electrical circuits by using adaptors inappropriately.

- Avoid using extension leads whenever possible.

Exercise 3.8

Promoting Fire Safety

Fire can cause panic to fit and healthy people. For people confined to wheelchairs or beds, or who have reduced mobility, a fire can be terrifying. These people will be depending on you for their safety.

Awareness of fire hazards is the first step toward prevention. Three elements are needed for a fire to start. By removing any of the following elements, a fire can be prevented or put out:

- **heat:** flame, spark, or other heat source

- **oxygen:** found in the air you breathe

- **fuel:** any combustible material (items that can catch fire and burn easily)

Alert the person-in-charge if you smell smoke. If a door feels hot, **do not open the door!**

Fire Hazards

Smoking: Never leave smokers unsupervised. Some people cannot handle smoking materials safely by themselves (due to medication, confusion, etc.).

Smoking materials (e.g., cigarettes, pipes, tobacco, matches) should be safely stored when not being used. Strictly enforce the smoking policy and follow these rules:

- Allow smoking in authorised areas only.

- Be careful when you empty ashtrays, not to set the rubbish bin on fire.

- Never allow paper cups or rubbish bins to be used as ashtrays. Ensure the ashtrays are non-combustible.

Exercise 3.9

Storage: Never store oily rags, paint cans, chemicals, or other combustibles in closed areas.

Electrical Equipment: Inspect all electrical equipment that you use and report any defects. Do not use faulty or potentially dangerous equipment, including the following:

- Frayed electrical cables
- Overloaded circuits
- Overheated equipment
- Improperly earthed equipment

Aerosol cans: Never burn aerosol cans. Never use an aerosol spray near open flames or cigarettes. Containers are likely to explode when they are exposed to heat. Never dispose of aerosol cans in rubbish bags that are to be incinerated.

In Case of Fire

Ensure that you know your organisation's emergency fire procedures.

- Understand fire evacuation procedures and designated assembly points where people can be counted to see if anyone is missing.
- Know locations of all exits and fire doors.
- Know where fire alarms and extinguishers are located.
- Know emergency telephone numbers.

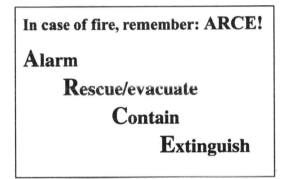

In case of fire, remember: **ARCE!**

Alarm

   Rescue/evacuate

      Contain

         Extinguish

1. Sound the **alarm**.

2. **Evacuate** the premises and rescue any people in immediate danger if it is safe to do so.

3. **Contain** the fire by closing doors and windows.

4. **Extinguish** the fire, if possible, using the correct extinguisher.

Exercise 3.10

Fire Extinguishers

Different types of extinguishers are used for different types of fires. Be sure you have the correct extinguisher for the fire, or you may make the fire worse and put yourself in danger.

Water (red)	For most fires, except those involving flammable liquids or live electrical equipment
Foam (cream/ yellow)	For burning liquids or electrical fires
Powder (blue)	For burning liquids or electrical fires
CO² Gas (black)	For burning liquids or electrical fires
Halon (green)	For electrical fires
AFFF (cream/ yellow)	For general fires, burning liquids or electrical fires. Use as directed for water or foam, depending on type of fire

In addition, there should be a fire blanket in the kitchen. The fire blanket can be thrown over the blaze (e.g., chip pan fire) to smother the fire and minimise fire damage.

Exercise 3.11 🖉

Gas Escapes

Whenever you can smell gas or you suspect that there is a gas leak follow these guidelines:

- Open all windows and doors to let in as much fresh air as possible.

- Do not do anything that might cause the gas to explode (e.g., light a cigarette, put a light switch on, turn the central heating on or off).

- Ensure the gas board are called on their emergency telephone number to alert them as quickly as possible to deal with the gas leak.

Bomb Scares

Most care organisations do not have policies or procedures to cover bomb scares. If you receive a warning that a bomb has been planted somewhere in the building, you must immediately inform the person in-charge. The person-in-charge is responsible for directing evacuation of the building, ensuring that everyone congregates at the specified assembly points so that they can be checked and counted, and informing the police of the situation.

Part 2: Maintaining Personal Health and Safety (CU1.2)

Never take risks with your health at work.

You have a responsibility to yourself, your family, your colleagues, and your employer to ensure that you do not take chances with your health at work.

Safe Lifting and Moving

The Manual Handling Operations Regulations came into force in the United Kingdom in 1993. The regulations provide clear guidelines on moving and lifting practice for employers and employees as well as a framework for risk assessment. Each care organisation will have interpreted these regulations in determining their own manual handling policies and procedures. Use only those lifting and moving techniques that are sanctioned by your employing organisation.

The regulations have placed an emphasis away from the old philosophy of "safe lifting" to a philosophy of avoiding manual lifting whenever possible. It is recommended that the approach to lifting and moving should focus on adapting the task to suit the skills and physical abilities of the individuals undertaking it. The expectation is that unavoidable handling tasks must be assessed in advance and action taken to remove or reduce the risk of injury to participants. The following factors should be taken into account during a risk assessment:

- The task
- The load—shape, size, weight, and stability
- The environment
- The individual capabilities of the staff

It is expected that this process should be documented and that if the task is deemed hazardous, mechanical lifting and handling aids should be made available. A lack of funds or resources is not an acceptable excuse for not providing the necessary training and equipment for manual handling.

Employers need to ensure that all care staff have access to a comprehensive education programme that includes the moving and handling of patients, minimising the risks and utilising the best equipment available. Updates on manual handling should be provided annually.

Exercise 3.12

Lifting and moving are still a major cause of accidents for care workers. If you have not completed a manual handling course covering relevant techniques and mechanical aids to lifting and moving, you should not become involved in the manual handling of clients. If you have received appropriate training, protect yourself and others from injury by using only the approved manual handling techniques and equipment. You should not undertake any manual handling of clients unless the necessary resources are available, except in emergencies. If you have concerns about the moving and manual handling techniques used in your area of work, contact your manager, your organisation's manual handling coordinator (if there is one), your local health and safety officer, or your occupational health officer.

The problem is more difficult when a client refuses to be moved using manual handling aids. Fortunately, a client does not have the right to cause injury to a carer by refusing the use of necessary equipment. If you encounter a problem in this area, seek advice from your manager.

Basic Handling Principles

Respect clients' wishes, whenever possible, when moving them or changing their positions. Maximise respect and dignity, and minimise any pain, discomfort, or friction during the move. If you need to change the environment to carry out the movement, ask the client's permission first. Then return the environment to its original state before you leave.

First, take a few seconds to assess the task at hand. Make sure that there is enough space to undertake the task, and prepare the environment for the move. Ensure that everybody involved in the task has received appropriate, recent training. Check the clothing and footwear worn by all participants to make sure that there is no hindrance to movement.

Tell the client what you are going to do, and encourage him or her to help and to be as mobile as possible. Ensure that privacy is maintained, where appropriate. Prepare the environment for the move.

One carer can lift up to 25 kg (3 st 13 lb for men), 16.6 kg (2 st 8 lb for women), and no more. Both of these values apply only to loads held close to the lower body. Ensure that your spine does not twist during

If, for any reason, you become involved in the disposal of "special waste" (e.g., radioactive materials, cytotoxic drugs), contact the infection control officer at your nearest NHS Trust.

The only exemptions to the duty of care in the management of clinical waste are for occupiers of domestic properties. The safe practice for disposal of waste by individuals in the community is provided in Module 6, Part 3.

Part 3: Responding to Health Emergencies (CU1.3)

Your prompt action can save lives.

Emergencies happen. Someone's life may depend on you. You must act fast if you are to save someone's life. Remember, though, that you can worsen the injuries of a casualty if you do not know what you are doing.

The following sections do not give a comprehensive account of first aid. Instead, they provide an overview of the basic skills. You need to attend a first aid course to learn the practice of first aid.

Exercise 3.21

Principles of First Aid

First aid is emergency care for a person who is ill or injured, before medical help arrives. First aid is given to prevent death or to keep injuries from getting worse.

- Act quickly, giving priority to the most urgent conditions.

- Check that there is no further danger to the casualty or to yourself.

- Check the casualty for responsiveness by gently shaking the shoulders and asking "Are you all right?"

- If the casualty responds, leave the person in the position in which you found him or her, as long as there is no danger.

- Reassess the casualty regularly, and position the person correctly.

- If the casualty does not respond, shout for help and check the airway.

- If breathing has stopped, clear the airway and begin cardiopulmonary resuscitation.

- Control bleeding.

- Guard against shock.

- Give reassurance to the casualty and to onlookers.

- If you must move the casualty, immobilise fractures and dress large wounds.

- If needed, get the casualty to hospital for medical treatment as soon as possible.

- Observe carefully for any changes in the casualty's condition.

- Do not try to do too much yourself.

- Do not give anything by mouth to a casualty who is unconscious or who may need an anaesthetic on arrival at hospital.

- Always record emergency incidents accurately and comprehensively in the prescribed format.

Exercise 3.22

Signs and symptoms of the different emergency situations may differ with the casualty's age and ethnicity. For example, an old person may fracture a femur (thigh bone) during a very minor fall, and not show the level of pain you would expect from a major leg fracture. Another example is difficulty in detecting bruising and pallor in people who have darker skins.

When someone requires first aid, other people tend to be drawn to the situation. Some may be concerned and would like to help. Others will simply have a morbid fascination for watching someone who requires first aid. Remember that health emergencies have an effect on anyone who is nearby, especially if they are a friend or relative (e.g., fear, anger, remorse). You may need to do the following:

- Send someone to get help.

- Ask onlookers to stand back to give the casualty air, to keep clear of any danger, and to give you plenty of room.

- Provide first aid to onlookers if they are shocked or faint.

- Ask for support when someone is feeling upset by the incident.

Recovery Position

The recovery position is used for casualties who have fainted or are unconscious. It is used to prevent the casualty from choking on the tongue or on vomit, especially if the person is unconscious and lying on his or her back.

1. If necessary, remove the casualty's spectacles.

2. Kneel beside the casualty and make sure that the legs are straight.

3. Open the airway by tilting the head and lifting the chin.

4. Tuck the arm nearest to you, well under the buttock on the same side, arm straight and palm uppermost.

5. Fetch the far arm across the chest, and hold the back of the hand against the casualty's nearest cheek.

6. With your other hand, grasp the far leg just above the knee and pull it up, keeping the foot on the ground.

7. Keeping the hand pressed against the cheek, pull on the leg to roll the victim toward you onto the side.

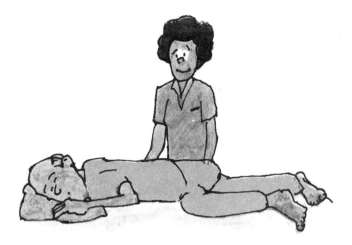

8. Adjust the upper leg so that both the hip and knee are bent at right angles.

9. Adjust the lower arm so that the casualty is not lying on it and the palm is still uppermost.

10. Tilt the head back to make sure the airway remains open.

11. Adjust the hand under the cheek if necessary, to keep the head tilted.

12. Check breathing.

Exercise 3.23 🖉

Shock

All casualties experience a certain amount of shock. It is important for you to recognise the signs and symptoms of shock.

- The casualty feels sick, vomits, or may be thirsty.

- The skin is pale, cold, clammy, and may be sweating.

- Breathing becomes shallow and rapid with yawning and sighing.

- Pulse rate becomes quicker, but weaker.

- Unconsciousness may develop.

59

The treatment for shock aims at getting an adequate supply of blood to the brain and vital organs. Follow these guidelines for treating shock:

- Reassure the casualty.

- Place in the recovery position if the person becomes unconscious.

- Lay the casualty down, and raise the legs if possible.

- Loosen tight clothing to help circulation and breathing.

- Moisten the lips if the casualty is thirsty (but do not give anything to drink).

- Avoid moving the casualty unnecessarily.

- Begin cardiopulmonary resuscitation if breathing or heartbeat stops.

- Get the casualty to hospital as soon as possible (unless the casualty has simply fainted).

Exercise 3.24 🖉

Burns and Scalds

Burns are generally caused by dry heat, electricity, friction, or corrosive chemicals. Scalds are caused by moist heat (e.g., boiling water). The pain may be intense, especially with superficial burns. There is usually redness, and blistering occurs later. In addition, there is usually a great deal of shock.

Following are guidelines for treating burns and scalds:

- Remove anything that constricts (e.g., rings, clothes, shoes) before the burned area begins to swell.

- Immerse the injured area in cold water or place under slowly running cold water for at least 10 minutes. This decreases the spread of heat and alleviates pain.

- Gently remove any clothing that has been soaked in boiling water. Burnt clothing has been sterilised and does not need to be removed.

- Lie the casualty down, and treat for shock.

- Cover the injured part with a clean, dry dressing.

- Give small amounts of cold drinks at frequent intervals if the person is conscious.

- Arrange for immediate removal to hospital for all but the most minor burns.

- Do not apply lotions or ointments.

- Do not prick blisters.

- Do not breathe over, cough over, or touch burned areas.

Bleeding

Major bleeding requires immediate treatment to save the person's life. External bleeding is easy to see, but internal bleeding may only show itself as the signs and symptoms of shock. The aim is to control the bleeding and to keep the wound free of infection. Following are guidelines for treatment:

- Uncover the wound and check for foreign objects. Do not touch any foreign object that is firmly embedded in a wound. Never pull out an object that has created a puncture wound (e.g., a knife).

- If there are no foreign bodies, apply direct pressure to the wound with the finger and/or hand, preferably over a sterile dressing.

- If the wound is large, squeeze the edges together to try to stop the bleeding.

- Lay the casualty down and treat for shock.

- If the wound is on a limb and there is no fracture, keep the limb raised.

- Place a sterile, unmedicated dressing over the wound and secure it firmly with a bandage.

- If the bleeding continues, apply additional dressings on top of the original dressing.

- If direct pressure does not stop the bleeding or if there is an embedded foreign body, use indirect pressure before continuing. To apply indirect pressure, press on the main artery that supplies blood to the limb (e.g., the brachial pressure point on the inside of the upper arm).

- Do not apply indirect pressure for more than 15 minutes at a time, and do not apply a tourniquet.

- Remove the person to hospital for treatment for all but the most minor cuts.

Exercise 3.25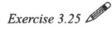

Choking

Clutching the throat is the universal sign for choking. When choking occurs, bend the person forward and give two or three hard slaps between the shoulder blades. Repeat if necessary. If the person is still choking, proceed with the **Heimlich Manoeuvre**.

Procedure for a conscious person:

1. Stand behind the person; slide your arms under the choking person's arms and wrap them around the waist.

2. Make a fist, and place it against the person's abdomen—below the rib cage and above the navel, being careful not to touch the sternum (centre breast bone).

3. Using your free hand, apply pressure against your fist with an inward and upward thrust.

4. Give four rapid thrusts, and repeat the procedure if necessary. The abdominal thrusts dislodge the obstruction upwards and out from the airway so the person can spit it out.

Procedure for an unconscious person:

When a person loses consciousness from choking, the neck muscles may relax enough for the object to no longer completely obstruct the airway. You may be able to remove the obstruction by scooping it out with your fingers.

If the airway is still blocked, follow these steps:

1. Call for emergency help.

2. Place the casualty onto his or her back.

3. Open the airway by tilting the head back and lifting the chin.

4. Check for breathing.

5. If there is no breathing, open the mouth to see if you can scoop the obstruction out with your fingers.

6. If the airway is still blocked, kneel beside or straddle the person at hip level.

7. Place the heel of your hand on the person's abdomen below the rib cage, with your fingers pointing towards the person's chest. Place your free hand over the positioned hand.

8. Position your shoulders over the casualty's abdomen, and thrust your hands inwards and upwards.

9. Give 6 to 10 rapid thrusts.

10. Check to see if the obstruction has been dislodged so that you can remove it from the mouth/throat.

11. Repeat steps 6 to 11, if necessary.

12. After the obstruction has been removed, if the person does not breathe or if the heart has stopped, start cardiopulmonary resuscitation.

Exercise 3.26

Cardiopulmonary Resuscitation

Cardiopulmonary resuscitation (CPR) training teaches valuable life-saving skills. The procedure uses mouth-to-mouth resuscitation and chest compression when the heart and/or the lungs have stopped working. Quick action is critical. CPR must begin as soon as the heart stops in order to prevent brain and internal organ damage.

Only fully trained people should administer CPR. If you have not already attended a course on CPR, you should attend a class as soon as possible.

The following information is NOT a CPR course. It is intended as an overview of the adult basic life-support guidelines for those who have completed CPR training. In this scenario, it will be assumed that you are alone and have found the casualty unresponsive to stimuli.

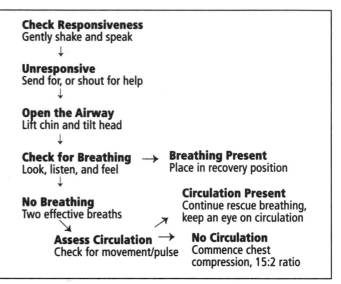

Flow Diagram of Basic Life Support

Following are CPR steps:

1. If possible, leave the victim in the position in which you found him or her. Open the airway by lifting the chin and tilting the head.

2. If this is difficult because of the position, turn the casualty onto the back. If a neck injury is suspected, try to avoid tilting the head.

3. If there is still no response, check for breathing (an occasional gasp should not be interpreted as breathing).

   • **Look** for chest movements.

   • **Listen** by putting your ear near the casualty's nose and mouth.

   • **Feel** for breath on your cheek.

4. Allow up to 10 seconds before deciding the casualty is not breathing. If breathing starts, put the casualty in the recovery position. Send for help if you have not already had the chance to do so, and reassess regularly.

5. If the casualty does not start breathing, if possible send someone for help and start rescue breathing. If you are on your own and cannot send someone for help, follow these guidelines:

    · If the casualty has been subject to trauma or drowning, or is an infant or child, this is usually due to primary respiratory arrest. In this case, give rescue breaths for about one minute (approximately 10 breaths) before reassessment; and, if the person starts breathing, go for help.

    · If the casualty does not fall into the above category, the cause of collapse is much more likely to be cardiac in origin, and defibrillation is the key to survival. Therefore, leave the casualty as soon as you have established that he or she is not breathing (rather than give rescue breaths) in order to get help. The casualty needs advanced life support.

6. Use precautions to prevent infection, if possible. (Remember, you are potentially at risk from *all* people.)

7. Tilt the head back by lifting the neck. Inspect the mouth for any obvious obstruction. Leave well-fitting dentures in place.

8. Pinch the nose closed to prevent air from escaping from the nostrils, and cover the casualty's mouth completely with your mouth.

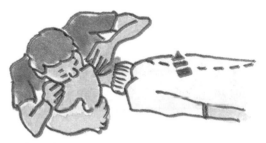

9. Blow into the person's mouth until you see the chest rise and fall. A breath volume of 400-500 cc is sufficient to provide adequate ventilation. Take about 1 1/2-2 seconds to breathe air into the casualty, resulting in an inflation/exhalation cycle of about 3-4 seconds.

10. After you have delivered two effective breaths of rescue breathing, assess the casualty for signs of circulation. Take no longer than 10 seconds to do this.

11. Look for movement such as swallowing or breathing.

12. Check the carotid pulse at the side of the neck. If the pulse is present, continue rescue breathing if necessary. Re-check for signs of circulation every minute, taking no longer than 10 seconds each time. If the casualty starts to breathe, but remains unconscious, put the person into the recovery position.

13. If there is no pulse, or if you are not sure, commence chest compressions—about 100 per minute.

    · Ensure that the casualty is lying on a firm surface.

- Locate the lower end of the sternum and place the heel of the hand over the end portion of the casualty's sternum.

- Then place the heel of your other hand over the top of the first hand to increase leverage.

- Use the heels of your hands to compress the chest.

14. Combine chest compression with rescue breathing at a rate of 15:2 if you are alone (or 5:1 if there are two of you). Only check the pulse again if the casualty moves or takes a spontaneous breath. Take no longer than 10 seconds to do this.

15. Continue resuscitation until the casualty shows signs of life or until qualified help arrives.

Exercise 3.27 🖉

Diabetes Mellitus

Diabetes mellitus is a medical condition where a person cannot produce enough insulin. Insulin is the hormone produced by the pancreas to help the body break down and convert sugars and starches into energy. Two complications of diabetes which require prompt attention are hyperglycaemia and hypoglycaemia.

Hyperglycaemia (diabetic coma) is the result of too little insulin or too much sugar. It occurs when blood sugar levels are high and there is an acidosis due to ketones being present in the blood. Although the onset of this condition is gradual, it is life-threatening and requires immediate medical care.

Early signs of hyperglycaemia:

- increased urination
- abdominal pain
- thirst
- nausea
- drowsiness

Later signs of hyperglycaemia:

- heavy breathing
- breath smells of pear drops
- dry skin
- flushed face
- loss of consciousness

Stay with the person to offer reassurance until the ambulance arrives to take him or her to hospital for treatment. At hospital, insulin is given to reduce the blood sugar, and sodium bicarbonate solution (an alkali) is given to counteract the acidosis and dehydration.

Hypoglycaemia (insulin shock) is the result of too much insulin or too little sugar. The onset of this condition is very quick as the lowered blood sugar affects the functioning of the brain.

Signs of hypoglycaemia:

- lethargy, weakness, dizziness
- hunger
- sweating
- confusion or bad temperateness
- trembling
- unconsciousness

Treatment includes giving glucose orally, as quickly as possible, before the person loses consciousness. In severe cases where the person loses consciousness, glucose is injected intravenously (into a vein) by a doctor. Stay with the person and offer reassurance until he or she recovers. This should happen very quickly after the glucose has been administered. Report hypoglycaemic attacks to the person-in-charge, and accurately record details of the attack (date, time, symptoms, speed of recovery, etc.).

If you are unsure whether a person who has diabetes mellitus is having a hypoglycaemic or hyperglycaemic attack, give the person glucose. If it is hypoglycaemia, recovery will happen very quickly. If it is hyperglycaemia, no harm will be done because it is the acidosis in hyperglycaemia that causes the major problems, not the raised blood sugar.

Exercise 3.28

Seizures

A seizure (fit) occurs when normal brain cell activity is interrupted by abnormal discharges of electricity within the brain. Seizures can happen to anyone. They are often caused by the following:

- tumours
- stroke
- infection and fever
- chemical imbalance
- head injury

Sometimes no cause can be found. When a person has seizures, even when they occur only occasionally, the person is said to have epilepsy.

The main treatment for epilepsy is medication (e.g., Epilim). Medication strengthens a person's resistance to seizures. It is important that people who suffer from epilepsy take their medication regularly, as prescribed. Medication completely controls epilepsy for some people; for others, seizures are kept to a minimum.

Generalised absence (petit mal) seizures are characterised by the person looking blank and staring. There may be slight blinking or twitching. This type of seizure lasts for only a few seconds. Afterwards the person continues as normal, as if nothing has happened, unaware of the seizure.

Complex partial (psychomotor) seizures may start with an "aura" or warning (e.g., seeing flashing lights or having a horrible taste in the mouth). The person appears confused or distracted and may repeat a series of movements (e.g., plucking at clothes).

Generalised tonic-clonic (grand mal) seizures tend to have a common sequence of events. However, not all tonic-clonic seizures will exactly follow the sequence. This type of seizure can last for several

minutes. It tends to be noisy and is very frightening for onlookers. There may be an aura followed by staring, followed by a stiffening of the body, which usually results in the person falling to the ground. The person may cry out. There may be a blue colour around the mouth and extremities. Eventually the person commences convulsions (jerking movements). As these fade away, breathing restarts and normal colour returns. There is often foaming at the mouth, and this can be blood-flecked. Occasionally, there is incontinence. The person may appear to sleep for a short while before regaining consciousness.

Exercise 3.29

Status epilepticus occurs when a person has repeated tonic-clonic seizures without recovering consciousness. This is a medical emergency. The person may die without prompt medical attention.

Do whatever is necessary to protect the person from injury during a seizure. Do not try to restrain the person. Never pry the mouth open, and do not insert anything into the mouth.

Care for tonic-clonic seizures:

- Do whatever is necessary to protect the person from injury.

- Try to support the person if he or she falls to the floor (be careful not to injure your back). If the person has not fallen to the floor, lie the person down.

- Move furniture and equipment out of the way to prevent injury during the convulsion stage of the seizure.

- If the person is in bed and there are side rails, pad the person with blankets or soft foam.

- Take care to protect the person's head from injury during a seizure.

- Do not leave the person alone during the seizure.

- If possible, turn the head to one side to prevent choking.

After a tonic-clonic seizure, be aware that the person will not remember the seizure. Reassure the person, and help the person to his or her feet.

If the seizure occurs in a care facility, follow these guidelines:

- Help the person to bed.

- Report all seizures to the person-in-charge.

- Chart the seizure, recording all relevant details (e.g., date, time, description of the seizure, length of recovery). Observe closely in case the person is confused or has another seizure.

Electrocution

Electrical injuries can kill or cause a wide range of injuries, including severe burns and heart stoppage. Most electrical accidents involve household appliances, but lighting circuits can have the same effect. The extent of injuries usually depends on the strength of the electrical current, how long the victim was exposed, and amount of insulation (e.g., whether the victim was wearing rubber-soled shoes or standing on a dry surface).

Never approach the victim of an electrical accident until you are sure it is safe. If the casualty is still in contact with the source of electricity, cut off the power supply before you touch the person by turning off the switch or unplugging the appliance.

If you cannot turn off the electricity supply because there are high voltage power lines, do not approach. You can receive a fatal shock up to 20 yards away. If it is household equipment that you cannot turn off and the casualty is still holding the source of electricity, stand on a rubber mat or dry newspaper, and lever the person's hand away using a wooden broom handle.

Once the casualty is safely removed from the electrical source, you can apply first aid. Smother any flames with a blanket or towel. If the casualty has been thrown to the ground by the electrical shock, check for breathing and pulse. Start CPR, if necessary. Then check that there are no fractures, and treat any burns. Electrical burns may be much deeper than their size suggests. Provide reassurance, and help as needed.

Exercise 3.30 🖉

Chest Pains

Chest pains can occur for a number of reasons. The most common cause of chest pain is angina. Angina is a severe, but temporary, attack of chest pain which is often induced by exercise. A person with chest pains will have a good idea whether the pain is angina or not. If it is angina, sit or lay the person down and help the person take a heart tablet (that angina sufferers usually have with them). The tablet is usually placed under the tongue and allowed to dissolve. At rest, the angina attack should soon disappear.

Chest pain could signal a heart attack. A heart attack is a potentially fatal reduction in blood supply to the heart. Signs of a heart attack include the following:

- Severe shock

- Severe and constricting chest pain, sometimes radiating down the left arm and left side of the neck

- Shortness of breath
- Weak and irregular pulse
- Unconsciousness

First aid for a heart attack includes the following:

- Provide reassurance.
- Put the casualty into the most comfortable position. This is usually sitting up (the best position to help breathing).
- Loosen tight clothing at neck, chest, and waist, and encourage deep breathing.
- Get medical attention as quickly as possible as the casualty needs urgent treatment.
- If the casualty becomes unconscious, check the pulse and respirations. Commence CPR if there is no pulse or respiration.

Exercise 3.31

Fractures

A fracture is a cracked or broken bone. There are two main causes of fracture—direct force (e.g., from a kick to the shin), and indirect force (e.g., falling on an outstretched hand and fracturing the collar bone).

The casualty may have heard the bone break. Crepitus can sometimes be heard (i.e., the sound of two broken ends of bone grating together). The casualty will probably not be able to use the affected part of the body, or it will be very painful to do so. The area of skin over the fracture will usually be swollen and bruised. The body part may be in an unnatural position or look different than the same body part on the other side of the body.

- **Simple fractures:** The skin is unbroken, and there may be heavy bruising.
- **Complicated fractures:** When there is damage to surrounding tissues (e.g., when a fractured pelvis punctures the bladder).
- **Compound fractures:** The bone protrudes through the skin, or the skin is lacerated

above the fracture leaving an opening for micro-organisms to enter.

- **Greenstick fractures:** The bone is bent and may half break. These fractures occur in children.

Treat all bone injuries as fractures until diagnosis proves otherwise. Move the casualty as little as possible. Make the person as comfortable as possible, handling with great care so that you do not increase injury, pain, and shock.

Gently remove clothing from any open wound over the break, and cover with a clean dressing. If a bone protrudes, pack around it so that the bandage used to hold the dressing does not press directly onto the bone. Immobilise the fracture if possible. There are many different ways of immobilising the different fractures. For example, put a broken arm in a sling or immobilise a broken leg by using the other leg as a splint. Remember to pad between bony prominences. Treat for shock and provide reassurance, and get the casualty to hospital as quickly as possible. Do not give anything to eat or drink.

Exercise 3.32

Poisoning

Poisoning is often accidental (e.g., a child who drinks bleach), but it can also be deliberate (e.g., a person who is trying to commit suicide).

A poison is a substance which, if taken into the body in sufficient quantity, can cause temporary or permanent damage. Poisons tend to be swallowed, inhaled, absorbed through the skin, or injected.

The signs and symptoms of poisoning vary greatly, depending on the poison, the method of entry, and the amount taken. Once in the body, the poison finds its way into the bloodstream where it is swiftly taken to all parts of the body.

A conscious casualty or onlooker may tell you that poisoning has occurred. When the casualty is unconscious, other features (such as a fume-filled room or empty tablet bottles) may tell you what you need to know.

The first aider should take the following steps:

- If the casualty is conscious, ensure an open airway and monitor breathing and circulation. If the casualty is unconscious, place in the recovery position.

- Prevent further injury from poisons:

Swallowed poisons: Do not attempt to induce vomiting as this may harm the casualty further. If the casualty's lips are burned by corrosive substances, give frequent sips of cold water or milk.

Inhaled poisons: Remove the casualty from danger into the fresh air. At work, do not enter gas-filled rooms unless you are authorised and properly equipped to do so.

Absorbed poisons: Flush away any residual chemicals on the skin, making sure that you do not get any on your skin.

- Obtain appropriate medical attention.

- Where appropriate, try to identify the poison.

Exercise 3.33 ✏

Summary

People in your care depend on you for their health, safety, and security. Your responsibilities include monitoring and maintaining each client's safety and security in the care environment. Vital skills for care workers include preventing accidents, minimising risks, and handling emergencies.

Two important principles for maintaining your own health and safety (as well as the clients') are lifting and moving, and infection control. Always follow safe lifting and moving procedures, and be sure you understand and adhere to principles of infection control.

Check Your Knowledge and Understanding

1. Jimmy, a resident on your day care unit, appears to be missing. He has wandered off the unit before and has put himself in danger. What should you do?

   a) Immediately implement the missing-person's procedure.

   b) Give him another hour to see if he wanders back to the unit on his own.

   c) Search the building thoroughly, and then search the grounds and local areas.

   d) Contact the police

2. You smell burning at work one day, although you cannot see a fire or any smoke. What would you do?

   a) Ignore the smell of burning as it may be coming from outside the building.

   b) Carry out a more thorough search for the source of the smell.

   c) Immediately raise the alarm and evacuate the building.

   d) Walk around the building to check that the fire extinguishers are all in working order.

3. You need to move a partially mobile person up in bed. Another carer who is a new member of staff comes to help you and states that she has not yet done the manual handling course, but she is willing to try a "drag lift." What would you do?

   a) Go ahead and use the drag lift because there is nobody else available to help you at the moment.

   b) Fetch a handling sling and show the new carer how to move the client up the bed.

   c) Lift the person up in bed by yourself.

   d) Gently explain that someone who has not yet completed the manual handling course should not be involved in the lifting and moving of clients. Wait until somebody else is available to help you.

4. An intravenous drug user, who is known to be HIV positive, is attending your day centre. Several of your colleagues claim that they are scared of catching AIDS. What would you do?

   a) Say, "I can understand your fears, but there is nothing you can do to stop this person attending the day centre."

   b) Suggest that your colleagues book in for an AIDS workshop.

   c) Advise them to see the day centre manager to express their fears and pick up copies of the AIDS leaflets.

   d) Tell them to stop being silly as they cannot catch AIDS from this person unless they have intimate sexual contact.

5. Someone comes to you who has just sustained a nasty burn to his hand from touching the steam iron. What would you do?

   a) Immediately apply a clean, dry dressing to prevent infection, after removing the person's rings in case the fingers blister.

   b) Immediately apply some antiseptic cream after removing the rings, but before you apply the dressing.

   c) Immediately put the person's hand under a slow-running tap, and gently slip the rings off the person's fingers.

   d) Prick the blisters as they start to form, and then apply a clean dry dressing.

6. A diabetic client, who is suffering from an ear infection, claims to be feeling unwell. He appears to be a bit confused and is sweating. What would you do?

   a) Quickly put a couple of glucose sweets into the person's mouth.

   b) Call for the doctor.

   c) Ask him to go to bed, and offer him an aspirin, saying you will check up on him later to see if he is any better.

   d) Advise the client to give himself more insulin.

Module 4

Undertaking Clinical Activities

Ensure the safe provision of clinical activities.

Objectives:

- Outline how to prepare for clinical activities.
- Describe how to undertake dressings and care of lesions.
- Outline how to undertake stoma care, catheter care, and tube feeding.
- Demonstrate extended personal care.
- Assist in the administration of medications.
- Explain how to obtain and test specimens.
- Discuss how to monitor the physical condition of clients.

Module 4 Introduction

Module 4 relates to four units of the level 3 NVQ/SVQ Award in Care:

Unit CU2: **Prepare and maintain environments for clinical procedures** is an option group B unit.

- CU2.1 Prepare environments for clinical procedures

- CU2.2 Maintain environments following clinical procedures

Unit X12: **Support clients during clinical activities** is an option group B unit.

- X12.1 Prepare clients for treatments, investigations, and procedures

- X12.2 Support clients during treatments, investigations, and procedures

- X12.3 Assist clients to recover from treatments, investigations, and procedures

Unit X13: **Undertake agreed clinical activities with clients whose health is stable in non-acute care settings** is an option group B unit.

- X13.1 Prepare clients for clinical activities

- X13.2 Undertake clinical procedures, treatments, and dressings

- X13.3 Obtain and test specimens from clients

- X13.4 Measure and monitor the physical characteristics and conditions of clients

- X13.5 Assist in the administration of client medication

Unit X19: **Prepare and undertake agreed clinical activities with clients in acute care settings** is an option group B unit.

- X19.1 Prepare clients for clinical activities

- X19.2 Undertake clinical procedures, treatments, and dressings

- X19.3 Obtain and test specimens from clients

- X19.4 Measure and monitor the physical characteristics and conditions of clients

Part 1: Taking Part in Clinical Activities (CU2, X12.1, X12.3 X13.1, X19.1)

Ensure that environments are prepared for clinical activities.

Different organisations have different rules and regulations that cover who is allowed, and who is not allowed, to undertake specific clinical activities. Also, make sure that you know the clinical activities which you are allowed to carry out within your organisation. Make sure that you read the relevant procedures, policies, or protocol for any clinical activity that you intend to undertake. If you need clarification, ask your manager.

Only the basic outlines of procedures and tests are provided within this textbook. Do not attempt any of the clinical activities outlined in this module until you have been assessed as being competent and are happy to undertake them. Whilst you are developing competence in an area of practice, a senior carer should provide you with the necessary level of supervision and teaching that you need to safely develop the new area of clinical competence.

Prepare the Environment

Follow these guidelines when preparing the physical environment for clinical activities.

- Make sure that you have **enough room.** Move furniture or equipment out of the way (with the client's permission) until you have finished. Then restore the environment to its original condition.

- Ensure that the clinical environment is kept **clean and tidy.** Do not allow mess and clutter to develop. Ensure that all equipment and materials are neatly stored (and locked, where necessary) in their cupboards and drawers.

- Depending on the clinical activity being undertaken and the personal preferences of the client, try to ensure that the **temperature** is acceptable and that there is enough light. Close windows, fetch an additional light if necessary, and keep the client covered as much as possible for warmth.

- When clinical activities are to be undertaken, particularly those of an embarrassing nature, make sure that **privacy** can be ensured for the client. Close curtains, use screens, lock doors, or use a "Do Not Enter" sign.

- The spread of **airborne infection** is most likely to occur following bed making and cleaning, which generally disperse microorganisms into the air. Preferably, these activities should be completed 30 minutes before an aseptic technique is carried out. To further reduce the risk of contamination of open wounds, curtains should be drawn around the bed 10 minutes before undertaking the aseptic technique. In addition, do not expose any wounds longer than necessary.

Exercise 4.1 ✎

Prepare Yourself

Following is a range of issues which you need to bear in mind for clinical activities:

- Ensure that you have the necessary competence to undertake the clinical task. Keep yourself up-to-date in terms of policies and procedures for your area of work (see Module 5, Parts 1 and 2).

- Ensure that you do not bring your emotional baggage to work with you. Be in the right frame of mind and mood to work and provide high quality care.

- Ensure that you are physically fit for the job in hand. For example, do not come to work if you have a severe cold, even if you feel guilty about taking time off work. Seek advice if you have an illness (e.g., HIV positive) or ailment (e.g., bad back) that might affect your ability to carry out your usual work roles.

- Ensure that you are well-groomed (e.g., dressed appropriately, not too much make-up, hair is combed), and that your personal hygiene is acceptable. Body odour and halitosis are unacceptable.

Exercise 4.2 ✎

Protective clothing is worn for a variety of reasons. Following are examples:

- To prevent the carer's clothing from becoming contaminated, soiled, wet, or stained during the procedure

- To prevent the transfer of pathogenic microorganisms from the carer to the client

- To prevent the carer from catching an infection from the client

Masks can be worn to prevent the spread of micro-organisms from the nose and mouth during breathing, coughing, and sneezing. A mask protects the wearer from inhaling airborne micro-organisms spread by an infectious client. You do not have to wear a mask routinely for aseptic techniques, although they are usually worn when caring for major burns victims.

Gloves are worn as part of the universal precautions against blood-borne viruses (see Module 3, Part 2). Sterile gloves allow a carer to undertake sterile procedures with his or her hands without contaminating the client or any of the sterile equipment.

Disposable plastic aprons are worn when there are likely to be copious amounts of fluid or exudate which may splash onto the carer's clothing or uniform.

In clinical areas such as operating theatres, all outer clothing and shoes need to be removed in the changing rooms prior to entering the "clean areas." Carers wear operating theatre greens (clothes) and boots (or clogs).

Exercise 4.3 🖎

Wash your hands before undertaking any clinical procedure or activity. Use bacteriocidal soap or bacteriocidal alcohol hand rub. For further information on washing hands and cross infection, see Module 3, Part 2.

Prepare Your Equipment

It is essential that you prepare your equipment prior to undertaking a clinical procedure or collecting/testing a specimen. This will prevent you from having to leave the immediate clinical area to fetch additional items of equipment which may result in the following:

- The client becoming embarrassed at being left in a compromising position
- The client being left exposed for longer than is necessary
- The nearby air being unnecessarily disturbed by curtains and doors when you are undertaking an aseptic technique

If you are undertaking a clinical procedure in a specially prepared clinical area, you need to ensure that all the necessary equipment is available before you take the client or the specimen to the clinical area. Alternatively, if you are taking equipment to a client, you will need to prepare a trolley or some other receptacle (e.g., a bowl) for transporting the equipment to the client.

The preparation of equipment includes ensuring the equipment you need is available, any lotions or sterile fluids are not out-of-date, and equipment is working properly. Ensure that there are always adequate stocks of necessary equipment available for carers to undertake clinical activities. One person should be made responsible for ordering clinical equipment and sterile supplies in order to maintain an adequate stock level whilst making sure that none of the equipment is out-of-date.

Exercise 4.4 🖎

Dressing Trolley

It is important that you clean dressing trolleys daily and every time they are used. Clean them with a detergent solution, and dry them carefully with clean paper towels. This removes a high proportion of micro-organisms, including bacterial spores.

Prior to using a trolley for an aseptic technique, wipe it over with chlorhexidine in 70 percent ethanol alcohol, using a clean paper towel. Trolleys used for aseptic techniques should not be used for any other purpose.

When preparing a trolley for an aseptic technique, follow these guidelines:

- Ensure that equipment and lotions are sterile and that packaging is undamaged before use.
- Place all equipment required for the procedure on the bottom shelf of the clean dressing trolley.
- Take the trolley to the treatment room or client's bedside, disturbing curtains or screens as little as possible.

Prepare the Client

Follow these guidelines, as appropriate, to prepare the client:

- Explain and discuss the procedure with the client in terms so that he or she knows precisely what to expect during the procedure. Use textbook diagrams and anatomical charts to help your explanation. Where possible, allay any fears about possible discomfort or pain during the clinical activity.

- Undertake any tests that need doing before the client undergoes the procedure (e.g., vital signs, blood sugar monitoring).

- Where appropriate, ensure that the client has a bath or shower before the procedure as the skin flora are an important source of infection during invasive procedures.

- Ensure the client has the chance to use the toilet before the clinical activity is started.

- Assess the client in terms of the ability to cope with, and willingness to cooperate during, the procedure. Check the client's plan of care to see if there is anything that you might need to look out for during the procedure. If you are likely to encounter problems in this area, you may need to modify the procedure.

- When necessary, take the client to the place where the clinical procedure is to be carried out, or the sample is to be taken. If it is to occur at the bedside, screen the bed.

- Always ensure privacy so that the client is embarrassed as little as possible during the clinical activity.

- Position the client comfortably for the procedure. Ensure that the area to be dealt with is easily accessible, without exposing the client unnecessarily. Take extra care when there is illness or restricted movement (e.g., due to pain), or when attached to equipment (e.g., drainage bottles, intravenous fluids, catheters and drainage bags).

Exercise 4.5 ✎

Support and Monitor the Client

During clinical procedures:

- Offer emotional support; some clients need very little support, others may need a lot. When in doubt, ask the client and use your observation skills.

- Keep monitoring the client during the procedure in terms of nervousness, stress, pain, or other symptoms (e.g., confusion or aggression).

- Hold the client's hand, and keep talking whilst the procedure or specimen collection is happening. Unless it is essential, do not leave the client alone.

- Explain to the client what you are doing at each stage of the procedure.

- When necessary, help the client to maintain a position or posture during the procedure. Ensure that the client is as comfortable as possible, and do not allow the client to become too hot or too cold.

After clinical procedures:

- Make sure the client is properly cleaned up after the procedure. If appropriate, encourage a wash, bath, or shower.

- Allow the client to get properly dressed, and then remove any curtains or screens. Return the client's environment back to its original state.

- Where necessary, help the client back to the chair or to bed, and make sure that he or she is comfortable.

• Where appropriate encourage the client to rest and recuperate after the procedure; if necessary, provide pain relief.

• Where necessary, keep monitoring the client in case there are any adverse reactions to the procedure (e.g., delayed shock).

• If the client has travelled to your care facility for the procedure, arrange transport and, if necessary, an escort to return home.

• Provide the client with any necessary information and advice that he or she needs to know before leaving. If available, provide the client and/or relatives with appropriate information leaflets, or arrange for health education if available.

Exercise 4.6 🖉

One problem that can occur after clinical procedures is that the client develops a hospital-acquired infection—an infection that was not present at the time of admission to hospital. The cost of hospital-acquired infections to the NHS is many millions of pounds. Therefore, hospitals employ infection-control teams to do the following:

• Reduce the likelihood of clients being exposed to infectious micro-organisms whilst in hospital.

• Provide policies that outline the care to be provided for clients who have infections that can be passed on to others.

• Minimise the chances of staff or visitors becoming exposed to infections.

• Provide education to staff so that they can help prevent or limit infections.

Part 2: Undertaking Clinical Procedures (CU2.1, X12.2, X13.2, X19.2)

You can effectively take part in a number of clinical activities.

A clinical procedure is any activity where a carer has to provide care that is specified by a local protocol, policy, procedure, or guidelines prepared by the employing organisation. Clinical procedures usually require the carer to have demonstrated clinical competence before he or she is allowed to undertake the procedure.

Aseptic Technique

Aseptic technique should be used during any invasive procedure that bypasses the body's natural defences (e.g., the skin and mucous membranes) or when introducing equipment such as urinary catheters into the body. It is used to prevent contamination of wounds and other susceptible sites by organisms that could cause infection. This is achieved by ensuring that only sterile equipment and fluids are used during invasive medical and care procedures.

A no-touch technique is essential to ensure that hands, even though they have been washed, do not contaminate the sterile equipment or the client. This can be achieved by the use of forceps or sterile gloves. The sterile supplies department normally provides all sterile instruments and equipment.

Exercise 4.7 🖉

Use the following guidelines:

• Clean wounds should be dressed before contaminated wounds. Colostomies and infected wounds should be dressed last of all to minimise the chances of cross-infection.

- Any equipment that becomes contaminated during a procedure must be discarded. On no account should they be returned to the sterile field.

- Dirty dressings should be carefully placed in a yellow clinical waste bag which is sealed before disposal.

- Keep air movement to a minimum during an aseptic technique—ensure nearby windows are closed, and discourage other people from moving about close to the area.

You will need the following equipment:

- A sterile dressing pack containing gallipots or an indented plastic tray, low-linting swabs or medical foam, disposable forceps, gloves, sterile field, disposable bag

- Fluids for cleaning and/or irrigation

- Hypo-allergenic tape

- An appropriate dressing or covering

- Any other materials that are needed because of the nature of the dressing (these should be highlighted in the client's plan of care)

Follow these procedures:

1. Wash your hands with bacteriocidal soap and water or bacteriocidal alcohol hand rub.

2. Check that the dressing pack and all other packs that are to be used are still sterile (i.e., undamaged, intact, and dry). If the pack has autoclave tape, check that the tape has changed colour from beige to brown and beige lines.

3. Open the outer cover of the sterile pack, and slide the contents onto the top shelf of the trolley.

4. Open the sterile field, using only the corners of the paper.

5. Open up any other sterile packs that you are using, and tip their contents onto the centre of the sterile field, ensuring that you do not contaminate them in the process.

6. Wash your hands again with bacteriocidal alcohol rub.

7. Using the forceps in the pack, arrange the sterile field, placing the handles of instruments towards the corners or edges of the field.

8. If appropriate, swab the edges of the lotion sachet with chlorhexidine in 70 percent spirit or a swab saturated with 70 percent isopropyl alcohol. Tear open the sachet and pour lotion into the gallipot or indented tray.

9. If appropriate, put on the sterile gloves, ensuring you touch only the inside of the wrist end of each glove.

10. Carry out the procedure, making sure the client is as comfortable as possible.

11. Dispose of waste in a yellow plastic clinical waste bag.

12. Check that the trolley is still dry and clean. If necessary, wash the trolley with liquid detergent and dry thoroughly with a paper towel.

13. Wash your hands with soap and water.

Exercise 4.8 🖉

Changing a Simple Wound Dressing

Use an aseptic technique for changing a wound dressing. Follow the procedure for aseptic technique up to step 5, and then follow these procedures:

1. If appropriate, loosen the old dressing and wash your hands again with bacteriocidal alcohol rub.

2. Using the forceps in the pack, arrange the sterile field, placing the handles of instruments towards the corners or edges of the field.

3. If appropriate, swab the edges of the lotion sachet with chlorhexidine in 70 percent spirit or a swab saturated with 70 percent isopropyl alcohol. Tear open the sachet and pour the lotion into the gallipot or indented tray.

4. Remove the dressing by putting your hand inside the plastic bag before lifting off the used dressing and inverting the plastic bag so that the dressing is inside the bag. Attach the bag to the side of the trolley below the level of the top shelf so that it can be used as the waste bag.

5. Assess the wound, noting rate of healing, signs of infection, etc. If unsure, have the wound assessed by a care professional. The results of the wound assessment should be accurately documented in the care record.

6. Put on the sterile gloves, using the no-touch technique.

7. If necessary, clean the wound with a gloved hand using 0.9 percent sodium chloride solution (unless another solution has been prescribed), and dry the wound with the non-linting swabs. Use each swab only once, ensuring that you wipe away from the wound. Where appropriate, flush the wound with the 0.9 percent sodium chloride solution, using a small sterile syringe.

8. Cover the wound with the most appropriate dressing (or the dressing that has been prescribed by the doctor) in order to promote healing.

9. Remove the gloves, and secure the dressing in place with hypoallergenic tape, netelast, or bandage.

10. Continue with steps 10-13 from the aseptic technique procedure (page 77).

Exercise 4.9

Stoma Care

A bowel or urinary stoma is usually created by a surgeon (e.g., colostomy, ileostomy, urostomy) on the abdominal wall because the urinary or colonic tracts beyond the position of the stoma are damaged and no longer viable due to trauma or disease. The stoma usually appears like a slightly protruding pink/red rosebud on the abdomen. It is positioned on the abdomen so that it can be easily managed by the client. The stoma is the opening for the excretion of bowel contents or urine, depending on the operation that has been performed.

Stoma care usually focuses on the following:

- Collecting urine or bowel contents into an appropriate stoma appliance

- Maintaining good skin and stoma hygiene

- Ensuring client comfort and security with the stoma and appliances

Some clients have problems after the formation of their stomas (e.g., coming to terms with the fact that their bodies look and function differently; having difficulty coping with the stoma appliances, care, and associated smells). Clients are not usually discharged from hospital until they are confident in providing their own stoma care. Many are provided with continuing support in the community.

In terms of diet, people who have urostomies are encouraged to maintain an adequate fluid intake that will flush the kidneys and help to prevent urinary infections. Clients who have colostomies or ileostomies are encouraged to eat as normal a diet as possible. They will find out which foods (e.g., large portions of fruit and vegetables) cause diarrhoea and flatus or wind, and regulate their diets accordingly. No two people react the same way to the same foods.

The main cause of distress for a client who has a bowel stoma is leakage and smell. The bowel contents tend to be very malodorous. Fortunately, when appliances are fitted correctly, the client can remain odour-free. Flatus is released via charcoal filters, and deodorisers are available. Any problems that do occur can usually be solved by the use of alternative appliances.

Exercise 4.10 🖉

Many of the **appliances** that are available to people who have stomas are very similar in style and effectiveness. The most essential aspect of an appliance is choosing one that is the correct size for the stoma. The skin surrounding the stoma needs to be protected from the stoma output which can be very irritating to the skin. Therefore, the appliance should fit snugly around the stoma to within 0.5 cm of the stoma edge. The small gap prevents the rigid appliance or its adhesive from damaging the sensitive stoma. A stoma size may change over time, requiring a change in size of appliance. The appliance should be leak proof and odour proof, unobtrusive (not bulky, not visible under clothes), noise free, and disposable.

There are two main types of appliances. The all-in-one consists of a bag with an adhesive wafer around the flange that fits around the stoma. As the bag is removed, the adhesive is separated from the skin. The two-piece appliance consists of a flange that fits around the stoma and a detachable bag. This type of device allows (potentially) sore skin to remain undisturbed. Some bags can be emptied (rather than disposed).

Stoma Bag

The stoma is not a wound. Therefore, mild soap and water are the best cleaning agents for the stoma and surrounding skin.

Follow these steps for changing a stoma appliance:

1. Collect the necessary equipment— clean tray containing tissues, new appliance and relevant accessories (e.g., filter), disposal bag, bowl of warm water and soap, jug (for contents of the old appliance), and gloves.

2. Position the client to view the procedure, and place a small protective pad so that any fluid leakage does not soil the client's clothing.

3. Put on the gloves; if the bag is drainable, drain the contents into the jug before removing the appliance.

4. Remove the appliance by gently peeling the adhesive off the skin, and remove any mucus or faeces from the stoma area with a damp tissue.

5. Assess the stoma and surrounding skin for ulcers or soreness. Anything unusual should be reported to the person-in-charge.

6. If everything appears to be in good condition, proceed by gently washing the stoma and surrounding skin, and then gently and thoroughly, drying them.

7. Apply a clean appliance. (You can remove your gloves for this task).

8. Remove and dispose of all used equipment.

  • In a care facility, the bag should be rinsed with water in the sluice, wrapped in a disposable bag, and placed in an appropriate waste bin.

  • In a client's home, the bag should be emptied down the toilet (the end of a closed bag has to be cut off with scissors), and the bag flushed out with water from a jug or by holding it under the toilet's flushing water. The bag should be wrapped in newspaper, double wrapped in plastic bags, and disposed of with the rest of the household rubbish.

9. Wash your hands thoroughly, using bacteriocidal soap and water or bacteriocidal alcohol hand rub.

Exercise 4.11 ✎

Catheter Care

Urinary catheterisation is defined as when a special tube (catheter) is inserted into the urethra and through to the bladder, using an aseptic technique. Once the catheter has been inserted into the bladder, a small balloon is inflated at the end of the catheter to prevent it from falling out.

Following are the main reasons for using a urinary catheter for a client:

- To empty the contents of the bladder (e.g., prior to pelvic surgery)

- To bypass an obstruction and relieve retention of urine

- To measure bladder output accurately

- As a last resort, to relieve incontinence

The most common sites for introducing an infection into a catheterised client can be seen in the diagram below.

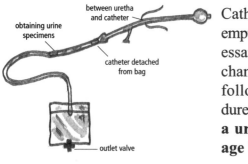

Catheter Bag

Catheter bags are emptied when necessary, rather than changed. Use the following procedure for **emptying a urinary drainage bag**:

1. Collect the necessary equipment—swabs saturated with 70 percent isopropyl alcohol, clean jug, disposable gloves.

2. Wash your hands with bacteriocidal soap and water or bacteriocidal alcohol hand rub and put on the disposable gloves.

3. Clean the outlet valve with a swab saturated in 70 percent isopropyl alcohol before emptying the contents of the bag into the jug.

4. Close the outlet valve and again clean it with a new swab saturated in 70 percent isopropyl alcohol.

5. Cover the jug, and get rid of the contents in the sluice having first noted the volume of urine, if this is needed for fluid balance records.

6. Wash your hands with bacteriocidal soap and water.

Keep the urethral meatus as clean and dry as possible in order to reduce the risk of infection entering the urinary tract.

Exercise 4.12 ✎

Tube Feeding

Tube feeding is used for clients who cannot eat or drink orally (e.g., due to cancer of the throat, inability to swallow). Prior to the tube being passed to enable nutritional support, the client should be nutritionally assessed. This includes the use of scales to measure the client's weight. The client's weight should be compared to his usual weight, rather than to weight/height charts. Percentage weight loss is a good guide to a person's nutritional status.

$$\% \text{ of weight loss} = \frac{\text{usual weight - actual weight}}{\text{usual weight}} \times 100\%$$

An unintentional or unexpected weight loss over six months of 10 percent can be defined as malnutrition and 20 percent as severe malnutrition. When there is obesity and/or oedema, this makes the estimate of weight loss much more difficult.

There is a number of other measures that may make it possible for a person to obtain sufficient nutrients without having to resort to tube feeding. Following are examples.

- Timing and frequency of food and drink
- Altering food consistency (e.g., liquidising food so that it can be easily swallowed)
- Altering food choices
- Providing dietary supplements

Exercise 4.13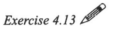

Naso-gastric feeding is the most commonly used type of tube feeding. But it tends to be used only in the short-term. If long-term tube feeding is required, an operation is usually carried out so that a tube can be passed through the abdominal wall into the stomach.

The naso-gastric tube is passed into the nostril, down the back of the throat, and into the stomach. The end of the tube protrudes from the client's nose, is usually taped to the cheek, and is stoppered with a spigot when not in use. Fine-bore tubes are used as they are more comfortable for the client and less likely to interfere with swallowing or cause irritation to the nose, throat, or oesophagus.

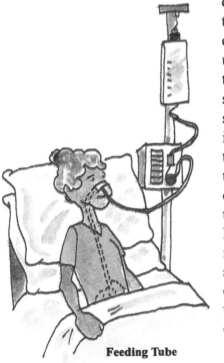

Feeding Tube

Commercially prepared feeds should, preferably, be used for tube feeding. This is to ensure that the client receives all the nutrients needed to maintain health. They also have the advantage of being sterile when packaged. The feed that the client requires is usually chosen either by a doctor or a dietitian, and is usually attached to a giving set so that it can be given by gravity drip or attached to a pump (depending on what the client can tolerate). The giving set and naso-gastric tube should be rinsed out daily by running plain water through the system, or the giving set can be replaced, whatever is advised in the manufacturer's instructions.

When not receiving a tube feed, the client should be disconnected from the giving set, and the naso-gastric tube should have a spigot pushed into the end so that it doesn't leak. When the client is to have tube feeding, follow this procedure:

1. Collect the necessary equipment—bag or bottle of prepared feed, and giving set (if required).

2. Position the client in a semi-upright position in bed or a chair. Support the head with pillows if necessary.

3. Wash your hands with bacteriocidal soap and water or bacteriocidal alcohol hand rub.

4. Flush the feed through the giving set before attaching to the naso-gastric tube. The pump can then be switched on, or the feed can be hung on an IV stand so that gravity allows the feed to slowly drip through the system.

5. If the client is being continually drip fed, leave all equipment in place ready for the next bag or bottle of feed.

6. If the client is being fed intermittently, disengage the naso-gastric tube from the giving set and put the spigot in the end of the tube. Dispose of all used equipment.

7. Wash your hands with soap and water.

Exercise 4.14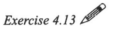

Part 3: Providing Extended Personal Care (X12.2/3, X13.2, X19.2)

Help others to care for themselves.

Hygiene can be described as the practice of providing a level of cleanliness that has a positive effect on health. Always encourage people to continue self-care, where possible. Unfortunately, people who are very young, very ill, very confused, or very disabled may have trouble maintaining their own hygiene. Bear in mind that hygiene and cleanliness are not luxuries, they are basic human rights.

Some people choose lifestyles that can best be described as unhygienic (e.g., people who choose to eat discarded food from litter bins and refuse to wash). Many people have some aspects of their lives that are unhygienic (e.g., forgetting to wash their hands before eating food). Everyone has their own (different) standards of "hygiene" that develop according to the person's life experiences, culture, religion, etc. Therefore, when caring for others, you should accept their hygiene standards, rather than trying to impose your own onto them.

It is appropriate, though, to intervene when a person's standards of hygiene are dangerous to themselves or others (e.g., coughing over food that they are preparing for others) or socially unacceptable (e.g., their body odour is making the other people feel sick). In these cases you should try to persuade the person to accept some health education or support in undertaking personal hygiene. The carer's role is to try and achieve a "mutually acceptable" level of cleanliness. If the client refuses to change unacceptable personal hygiene habits, seek advice.

Privacy is also a basic human right. For some cultures (e.g., Moslem), modesty is very important. It can cause problems when a client cannot manage his or her own personal hygiene and needs to depend on another person for help. Most people feel a sense of embarrassment when another person is required to help them, or undertake for them, some aspect of their

personal hygiene or toiletting that would normally be very private.

In care establishments, there can be common use of care equipment (e.g., bowls, cloths, towels, nail scissors). If these are not changed or thoroughly cleansed between clients, there is a serious risk of cross-infection. Where possible, each client should have his or her own toiletries, towel, bowl, etc.

Exercise 4 15

Bed Bath

Where possible, the client should manage his or her own personal hygiene. When a client cannot leave the bed to use the bath or shower, a bed bath is required. Ensure that you find out the client's personal preferences for personal hygiene and self-care abilities before commencing the bed bath. The bed bath is an excellent opportunity for communicating with the client and assessing the client's physical condition.

Follow these steps for a bed bath:

1. Collect all necessary equipment at the bedside—clean bed linen, bath towel, laundry skip, towel(s), toiletries, clean night clothes, washbasin, and warm water.

2. Clear the area around the bed. Ensure privacy by pulling round curtains or screens and closing doors. Close all nearby windows to prevent draughts.

3. Allow the client the chance to use a bedpan, commode, or urinal.

4. Cover the client with a bath blanket over the bed clothes, and then pull the bed clothes down to the foot of the bed.

5. Fill the bowl with hot water, and commence by washing the hands and face; ask if soap is required. Any additional care of the mouth, eyes, ears, or nose can be given after the bed bath.

6. Remove the top half of the client's clothing so that the top half of the body can be washed, rinsed, and dried. Apply toiletries where requested.

7. Replace the clothing.

8. Change the water at this point (or at any other point in the bed bath if the water becomes cool or very soapy).

9. Remove the bottom half of the client's clothing (if necessary), ensuring that only those parts of the body that are being washed/dried are exposed. Wash, rinse, and dry the lower part of the body. Apply toiletries where requested.

10. Replace the clothing.

11. Change the bottom sheet whilst the client is being turned during the bed bath.

12. Where necessary, assist the client with dental hygiene, and provide help to comb or brush the hair.

13. Pull the bed clothes back up over the client, and remove the bath blanket.

14. Remove and dispose of all used equipment, and wash your hands.

Exercise 4.16 ✎

Care of the Mouth

Three main functions of the mouth are ingestion of food and water, communication, and breathing (in conjunction with the nasal cavity). The lips form the entrance to the mouth cavity which contains the cheeks, gums, tongue, and teeth. The mouth is lubricated by the secretions of the salivary glands (saliva), which protects the mouth and helps to digest food.

The aims of mouth care and oral hygiene include the following:

· Keep the lips and mucosal layer on the inside of the mouth clean, soft, moist, and intact, in order to prevent infection.

· Remove food debris, including dental plaque, without damaging the gums.

· Alleviate pain and discomfort whilst promoting the oral intake of food and fluids.

· Prevent halitosis (bad breath) and freshen the mouth.

Poor oral health can result in mouth ulcers, infection, bleeding gums, dental caries (tooth decay), difficulties in tasting, swallowing, speaking, and respiration. The main factors which tend to cause poor oral health include the following:

· Not taking adequate fluids

· Poor nutritional status

· Insufficient saliva production

· Lack of knowledge or motivation to maintain oral hygiene

Exercise 4.17 ✎

Mouth care includes an oral assessment which should indicate the type of oral care tools and agents that are required. The tools may include toothbrush, foamstick, dental floss, and gauze. Choose the tool that will clean the teeth well without damaging the gums. The toothbrush, in most cases, is the tool of choice. There is a wide choice of oral care agents, depending on whether the main aim is to remove food debris and plaque, prevent infection, alleviate pain, stop bleeding, or provide lubrication. For most people, the agent of choice is toothpaste.

To maintain good oral hygiene, a person needs to clean the teeth with a toothbrush and toothpaste after meals and floss regularly. Sometimes clients are unable to do this for themselves, and you will have to do it for them.

Occasionally, because of poor oral hygiene or because of illness, a client's mouth can become very dry and dirty resulting in smelly breath (halitosis) and a mouth infection. This requires more extensive mouth care. Follow these steps:

1. Assemble your equipment—clinically clean tray, plastic cups, mouthwash or mouth-cleaning solution (e.g., chlorhexidine gluconate 0.2 percent diluted in 100 mls of water), waste bowl or sink, paper tissues, wooden spatula, soft toothbrush, toothpaste, gloves, small torch, and denture pot.

2. Wash your hands with bacteriocidal soap and water or bacteriocidal alcohol hand rub, and dry with a paper towel.

3. Prepare the required solution for mouthwash.

4. Where appropriate, remove the client's dentures using a tissue.

5. Inspect the client's mouth with the aid of a spatula and small torch.

6. Using the toothpaste, gently but firmly brush his teeth, gums, and tongue. Always brush away from the gums.

7. Give a beaker of water or mouthwash to the client to rinse the mouth and spit the contents into the waste bowl or sink.

8. If the client is unable to do this, use a rinsed toothbrush on the teeth and moistened foam sticks for the gums and inside of the mouth, using a rotating action so that all the surface area is covered.

9. If necessary, apply artificial saliva to the tongue and a suitable lubricant to dry lips.

10. Clean the dentures on all surfaces using a denture brush or toothbrush and toothpaste. Rinse them, and return them to the client's mouth. If there is an oral infection, the dentures can be soaked in chlorhexidine solution for 10 minutes.

11. Remove all used equipment, and discard waste.

12. Wash your hands with soap and water or alcohol hand rub; dry with a paper towel.

Exercise 4.18 🖉

Care of the Eyes

The eye is protected by the bony cavity of the orbit, the clear conjunctiva which covers the front of the eyeball and the inside of the eyelids, the lacrimal (tear) apparatus, the eye brows, and the eye lashes.

Tears are produced in the lacrimal glands. The tears wash over the eye, removing foreign substances. Tears also contain an antiseptic enzyme (lysozyme). They drain out through a small hole (punctum) on the inner margin of the lower lid, near the nasal corner of the eye. The eye should always appear moist. Remember that the eye is very sensitive to touch. Occasionally, because of infection or inflammation, the tears form an exudate which can harden and form crusts on the eye lids. If left, these can irritate the eye.

To clean the eye, follow these steps:

1. Ensure that you have a sterile dressing pack and sterile water.

2. Position the client comfortably— lying down with the head tilted backwards and the chin pointing upwards.

3. Ensure that there is a good light source without it shining directly in the client's eye. Check that your positioning doesn't block out the light.

4. Wash your hands thoroughly with bacteriocidal soap and water or bacteriocidal alcohol hand rub, and dry them.

5. Always treat the uninfected, uninflamed eye first.

6. Start the procedure by bathing the eye with the lids closed.

7. Then, using a slightly moistened, low-linting swab, ask the client to look up and swab the lower lid from the nasal corner outwards. Ensure that the swab does not go inside the lid margin and touch the sensitive cornea.

8. Using a new swab each time, repeat the procedure until all the exudate has been removed.

9. Swab the upper lid by slightly everting the lid margin and asking the client to look down, swabbing from the nasal corner outwards and using a new swab each time.

10. After both eyelids have been cleansed and dried, make the client comfortable.

11. Remove and dispose of used equipment, and wash your hands.

Exercise 4.19 ✐

Care of the Skin

It is important to maintain a healthy skin. The skin has several functions which include the following:

- Maintaining temperature
- Protection
- Excretion (sweat and sebum)
- Sensation

Skin has three layers—epidermis, dermis, and a deep subcutaneous layer. The epidermis is on the outside. The cells on the surface are continually being rubbed off and replaced by new cells which grow from underneath. The epidermis has hairs, sweat glands, and the ducts of sebaceous glands protruding through it.

The initial stage of skin care is to observe the general condition of the skin. Several factors may influence the state of the skin:

- Level of **hydration/dehydration** causes the skin to appear inelastic and dry, and oedema causes stretching and thinning of the skin.

- **Age** can affect the level of elasticity in the skin, producing wrinkles and making it more prone to damage.

- **Health** status will also affect the skin (e.g., venous ulcers, pressure sores, wounds).

- **Skin conditions** can also affect the health of the skin (e.g., psoriasis, eczema).

Any skin problems should prompt you to take extra care during bathing procedures. Remember people's preferences for personal hygiene (e.g., some people do not like soap on their faces, especially if it tends to dry their skin). Some people prefer moisturisers and other creams applied to their skin.

Always take extra care with skin folds, creases, and crevices. Ensure that they are thoroughly cleaned, dried, and inspected for damage. Take care when washing and bathing clients who have dressings, intravenous lines, etc. Dressings/drainage tubes should be disturbed as little as possible. Keep them dry in order to prevent infection from being introduced to the sites.

Undertake a full assessment before deciding on the type of skin cleansing to use for an individual. Always encourage people to be self-caring, where possible. You can provide support and/or equipment, depending on the level of assistance required. Some cultures prefer to be cleansed under running water, rather than being sat in a bath.

Exercise 4.20 ✐

Perineal Care

Perineal care is the one area of hygiene that is most likely to cause embarrassment and humiliation. Ensure that this area of the body is kept meticulously clean and dry. This is especially important when the person has a problem with this area of the body (e.g., catheter, wound, diarrhoea).

Extreme care should be taken to ensure privacy and minimise embarrassment. Take into account the individual's personal preferences for perineal care.

Preferably, the personal hygiene of the perineum should take place after having a bath. If having a bed bath, the water should be changed and different wipes should be used after the perineum has been cleaned. Many micro-organisms live around this area of the body.

Exercise 4.21 ✐

Hair Care

The appearance of a person's hair can have a significant effect on that person's self-esteem. Some people wash and groom their hair every day. Others prefer to leave it alone for days or weeks at a time. Always take the time to find out a client's preferences for hair care.

Washing hair is quite an easy task unless a client is confined to bed. Even then, if you can get the client's head to the foot of the bed and hang it over the edge, it is possible to wash the hair. If hair washing is not feasible (e.g., due to a head wound), you can use an aerosol dry shampoo.

Grooming the hair provides an opportunity to assess the head and scalp for dandruff, wounds, head lice, etc. Remember that some religions insist that hair is neither washed nor brushed and other religions insist on the hair being covered (e.g., by a turban).

Remember the hair on other parts of the body. Some women prefer their axilla and other parts of their body to remain clean shaven/stubble free. Men may need help with the grooming/shaving of their facial hair.

Foot and Nail Care

Nails should be trimmed carefully and correctly, using appropriate nail trimmers/cutters. Take special care with the toenails. Many people have misshapen toes and toenails.

Some toenails can be very difficult to cut, requiring the specialist equipment of a chiropodist. If clients have problems with peripheral circulation due to diabetes for example, it is usually safer to always have their toenails cut by a chiropodist. When their toes are damaged, there are often significant delays in the healing process.

Always encourage clients to pay particular attention to their feet by cleaning and drying thoroughly between the toes to prevent fungal infections. If you notice any foot problems like corns, calluses, ingrowing toenails, etc., report these to the person-in-charge so that a chiropodist can be called in to treat them.

Exercise 4.22 ✐

Part 4: Administering Medications (X13.5)

Ensure that clients receive the correct medication.

The storage and administration of drugs is not simply a matter of following the written prescription of the doctor. Carers are expected to use their judgment to ensure the safety and well-being of clients.

Some general principles of storage can be applied to all medications:

- **Security:** To prevent unauthorised access and to deter drug misuse/abuse, drugs should be stored in a locked cupboard. If a drug trolley is used, it should be kept locked and secured to the wall.

- **Separation:** Medicines should be stored in a different cupboard to non-medicines. Oral and topical preparations should also be stored separately.

- **Drug stability:** Drugs should be stored where there are not substantial changes to temperature, and they should not be exposed to sunlight. Some preparations require specific conditions (e.g., in the refrigerator).

- **Containers:** Drug containers and packaging are specially chosen for the individual drug. Do not transfer drugs into different containers as this may affect the stability of the drug.

- **Labelling:** The labelling on all drug containers should be clearly printed to ensure that medications are used as prescribed.

- **Stock control:** Check that drugs are not "out-of-date" before using them. All drugs have a limited shelf life.

Exercise 4.23 🖉

Before administering medicines, check local policies to ensure that you are allowed to assist with this procedure. In hospitals, nurses are usually the only carers involved in administering medications. In other non-acute care environments (e.g., clients' homes, residential homes), support workers who have received appropriate training may be allowed to administer some medications. Where possible, clients should be encouraged to administer their own medications.

You need to have a sound knowledge of the usage, action, usual dose, side effects, and contra-indications of all the drugs that you administer. Ensure that you follow all local policies and procedures pertaining to the administration of medications. The majority of mistakes in administering drugs tend to be caused by procedural error. It is essential that you report all errors in the administration of medications to your manager.

People who are taking medications need to be monitored. No drug produces a single effect; the combined effect of two or more drugs taken together may produce effects that are different from those when the drugs are taken separately. You should note the effectiveness of all drugs and note any signs of tolerance or dependence. Be aware of the side effects of drugs. They can range from slight symptoms of nausea to severe reactions that can cause death.

Exercise 4.24 🖉

Follow these general guidelines for the administration of medications:

1. Before administering any prescribed drug, check the following:
   - The drug
   - The dose
   - The date and time of administration
   - The route of administration

- The validity of the prescription
- That the prescription or record chart is legible
- That it has not already been administered

2. Select the required medication, and check the expiry date.

3. Where appropriate, empty the required dose into a medicine container without touching either the dose that is to be administered to the client or the remainder of the medication in the container.

4. Take the medication and the prescription/record chart to the client. To prevent error, check the client's identity and the dose to be administered.

5. Where appropriate, assess the client's knowledge of the medication being administered. If necessary, offer an explanation of the use, action, dose, and potential side effects of the medication(s) involved.

6. After administering the medication, record the dose given on the prescription/record chart and in any other document required by local policy.

7. Wash your hands with bacteriocidal soap and water or bacteriocidal alcohol hand rub after administering drugs.

Exercise 4.25 🖎

Oral medication can be in the form of tablets, capsules, lozenges, pastilles, linctuses, elixirs, syrups, and mixtures. Offer the medication to the client to take it him/herself, and provide water to help with swallowing the medication. Where appropriate, check that the medication has been swallowed.

Remember the following details:

- Drugs which irritate the stomach should be administered with food or a snack.

- Drugs which interact with food should be administered between meals.

- You should not break a tablet unless it is scored.

- You should not interfere with time-release capsules. Clients should be asked to swallow these whole and not chew them.

- Sublingual tablets must be placed under the tongue, and buccal tablets between gum and cheek.

Inhaled drugs are usually given in two ways:

- Nebuliser: Air or oxygen is passed through a solution of the drug, creating a fine spray which is inhaled. Some antibiotics and bronchodilators are given this way.

- Aerosol: The drug is dissolved and passed through a valve under pressure which allows the delivery of a measured dose of the drug in a very fine spray. Steroids and bronchodilators can be delivered in this way.

Using an Inhaler

Follow these procedures for inhaled drugs:

1. Sit the client in an upright position, if possible.

2. Carefully demonstrate and explain the use of the equipment where necessary. It is essential that the nebuliser or aerosol is used according to the manufacturer's instructions. (Otherwise the treatment may be ineffective. The client will have most of the dose remaining in the mouth, or the drug will be expelled almost immediately, or not enough of the drug will reach the client's lungs.)

3. Administer only one drug at a time, unless given specific instructions to do otherwise.

4. Clean the equipment after use.

Exercise 4.26 ✎

Eye, Nose, and Ear Preparations

Use the following procedure to administer **eye drops/ointment:**

1. Ensure that you have the required eye drops/ointment and some low-linting swabs. Aseptic technique is needed only when the eye is damaged or following ophthalmic surgery.

2. Position the client comfortably—lying down with the head tilted backwards and the chin pointing upwards.

3. Ensure that there is a good light source without it shining directly in the client's eye. Check that your positioning does not block out the light.

4. Wash your hands thoroughly with bacteriocidal soap and water or bacteriocidal alcohol hand rub, and dry them.

5. If there is any discharge, clean the eye. (See "Care of the Eyes," Part 2 of this module.)

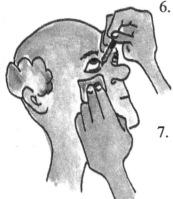

6. Place a low-linting swab on the lower lid against the lid margin to absorb any excess solution that may be irritating to the surrounding skin.

7. For eye drops, ask the client to look up immediately before instilling the drop(s). For eye ointment, slightly evert the lower lid by pulling on the low-linting swab before asking the client to look up and

inserting a line of ointment from the nasal corner outwards. Make sure the eye dropper or eye ointment nozzle does not touch the eye.

8. Ask the client to close the eye, keeping the low-linting swab on the lower lid against the margin. For eye ointment, remove excess ointment with a new low-linting swab, and remind the client that vision is likely to be blurred in that eye for a few minutes.

9. Make the client comfortable.

10. Remove and dispose of equipment.

11. Wash your hands with bacteriocidal soap and water.

Use the following procedure for **nasal drops:**

1. Ensure that you have the nasal drops and some tissues and/or some damp cotton buds handy.

2. If necessary, clean the client's nasal passages with tissues or a damp cotton bud.

3. Ask the client to put his or her head back so that the nostrils are pointing upwards.

4. Using the nasal dropper, drop the required number of drops into the client's nostrils, without touching the nostrils with the dropper.

5. Ask the client to maintain his or her position for 1-2 minutes. (It can be uncomfortable to maintain this position for more than a couple of minutes).

Use the following procedure for **ear drops:**

1. Ask the client to lie on his or her side with the ear that is to be treated uppermost.

2. Warm the ear drops to body temperature, if allowed.

3. Take hold of the ear, and pull it gently backwards and upwards to make it easier for the drops to reach their target.

4. Using the dropper, drop the required number of drops into the external canal, without touching the ear with the dropper.

5. Ask the client to remain in this position for 1-2 minutes.

Exercise 4.27

Vaginal and Rectal Preparations

Medications for vaginal and rectal areas of the body are usually in the form of an enema, suppository, or pessary. The procedure for an enema is given in Module 7, Part 1. Follow this procedure for the administration of a suppository or pessary:

1. Collect the necessary equipment at the bedside on a tray or trolley—disposable incontinence pad, disposable gloves, swabs or tissues, lubricating jelly, suppository, or pessary.

2. When possible, for suppositories, ensure the client has emptied his or her bowels and ensure that a bedpan, toilet, or commode is nearby.

3. Assist the client to lie in the left lateral position (i.e., on the left side with the knees flexed and the buttocks near to the edge of the bed). An additional position for pessaries is for the client to lie on the back with knees drawn up and legs parted.

4. For a suppository, place the disposable incontinence pad underneath the client's hips and buttocks.

5. Wash your hands with bacteriocidal soap and water or bacteriocidal alcohol hand rub, and put on the gloves.

6. Squeeze some lubricating jelly on a swab or tissue, and lubricate the blunt end of the suppository or the pointed end of the pessary.

7. For the suppository, separate the client's buttocks and insert the suppository, *blunt end first*, gently pushing it in 2-4 cms with the index finger. A pessary should be inserted into the top of the vagina (preferably in the evening when the client is not going to get out of bed).

8. Clean excess lubricating jelly from the client's anal area (suppository) or vulva (pessary) with a tissue.

9. Make the client comfortable, and ask the client to retain the suppository. Apply a clean sanitary pad to the client who has had a pessary inserted.

10. Remove and dispose of equipment, and wash your hands.

Topical Medications

Topical medications can be in the form of cream, ointment, or lotion. Use the following procedure:

1. Collect the necessary equipment (e.g., flat wooden spatulas, sterile swabs, gloves).

2. If the preparation causes staining, you must explain this to the client.

3. Put on the gloves.

4. Remove the preparation from the container using a spatula or sterile swab. Use a different spatula or swab each time if more of the preparation is needed.

5. If the medication is to be rubbed into the skin, it should be placed on a sterile swab and rubbed in with the swab.

6. Use an aseptic technique if skin is broken.

Exercise 4.28

Part 5: Obtaining and Testing Specimens (X12, X13.3, X19.3)

Competently obtain and test specimens that you have taken from clients.

Specimen collection can be defined as the collection of a desired amount of tissue, fluid, or other body material for laboratory examination. Specimens are collected when investigations are required to establish the baseline of a client's health or illness, assess the course of an ongoing illness or condition, or assess the effectiveness of treatments.

Successful testing of specimens is dependent upon the collection of the correct specimen at an appropriate time, using the correct technique, and despatching the specimens to a place where they can be tested without delay.

Follow these general guidelines when **collecting specimens:**

- Ensure that you have a request form completed by an appropriate care professional, where appropriate, before collecting the specimen.

- Collect all necessary equipment before taking the specimen (e.g., sterile specimen containers, spatulas).

- Wash your hands using bacteriocidal soap and water or bacteriocidal alcohol hand rub.

- Place all specimens, where appropriate, into correctly labelled specimen containers, and promptly despatch them to the laboratory. (Alternatively, test all appropriate specimens within the clinical area immediately.)

Exercise 4.29

Collecting Specimens

Urine is formed by the kidneys, which manufacture approximately 2.5 litres per day. It is characteristically clear, pale to deep yellow in colour, and slightly acidic (pH6). The pH can change as a result of what is consumed in the diet and because of health problems (e.g., vomiting and bacterial infection of the urinary tract can cause the urine to become alkaline).

Fresh urine smells slightly aromatic, but this can change as a result of disease processes like diabetes mellitus when the urine contains acetone which gives it a fruity smell. The composition of urine can change dramatically because of disease processes. It can contain red or white blood cells, glucose, protein or bile. The presence of these urinary abnormalities can be an important warning sign of illness.

A specimen of urine for urinalysis should be collected in a clean container (e.g., a jug). Specimens of urine are usually collected as soon as possible after the client wakes up in the morning. Try to collect it at the specified time each day if more than one specimen is required.

Exercise 4.30

Sometimes, you will need to collect a **mid-stream specimen** of urine. Follow these guidelines for a mid-stream specimen:

1. Ensure you have a sterile container (e.g., jug) and a sterile specimen container.

2. Ask the client to carefully clean the labia and urethra (female) or the glans of the penis (male) with soap and water (not antiseptic) in order to reduce contamination of the urine specimen to a minimum.

3. The client should be sat on a commode or stood in a position so that either you or the client can catch the specimen.

4. Allow the client to pass urine for a few seconds (to flush out any bacteria present in the urethra) before placing the sterile container beneath the stream of urine so that you can catch the remainder.

5. Transfer an appropriate amount of the urine into the sterile specimen container, taking care to not contaminate the inside of the container. Seal it immediately, making sure that it is clearly labelled. Despatch it to the laboratory with an appropriately completed request form, at the earliest opportunity.

6. Dispose of all used equipment, and wash your hands.

Follow these guidelines for taking a **catheter specimen of urine**:

1. Collect the necessary equipment—swab saturated with 70 percent isopropyl alcohol, gate clip, sterile syringe and needle, sterile specimen container.

2. If there is no urine in the catheter bag tubing, clamp the tubing below the level of the rubber cuff until urine collects in the tubing.

3. Wash your hands in bacteriocidal soap and water or bacteriocidal alcohol hand rub.

Gloved hands

Marked segment of rubber

Sterile syringe and needle

Clamp

Taking Urine from Catheter

4. Clean the rubber cuff with 70 percent isopropyl alcohol. Then, using a syringe and needle, remove the required volume of urine and place the specimen in the sterile container.

5. Unclamp the tubing (if necessary), and then wash your hands with bacteriocidal soap and water.

6. Label the container, and send it with the completed request form to the laboratory.

Check the manufacturer's instructions to find out the maximum number of times that a urine sample can be taken from the cuff of the catheter bag tubing.

Exercise 4.31 ✎

When collecting a **specimen of faeces**, use the following guidelines:

1. Collect the necessary equipment—(e.g., bedpan, spatula, sterile specimen container).

2. Ask the client to open his bowels into a clinically clean bedpan.

3. Scoop enough of the faeces out of the bedpan to fill at least one-third of the specimen container. Seal it immediately, making sure that it is clearly labelled. Despatch it to the laboratory with an appropriately completed request form, at the earliest opportunity.

4. In addition, you can examine the rest of the specimen in the bedpan for amount, size, consistency, colour, odour, and any abnormalities (e.g., foreign bodies, worms). Immediately document and report any abnormalities that you see.

5. Dispose of all used equipment, and wash your hands.

When collecting a **specimen of sputum**, use the following guidelines:

1. Collect necessary equipment together (e.g., a clean–not sterile–specimen container).

2. Ask the client to cough deeply and spit the sputum into the container. Ensure that the exudate (fluid that oozes through the walls of small blood vessels) sent for investigation is sputum, rather than saliva.

3. If the client has difficulty coughing up sputum, ask him or her to produce a specimen on waking in the morning. Ask the person to breathe deeply and cough hard. If problems continue, ask a physiotherapist for help.

4. Make sure that the sputum specimen is clearly labelled, and immediately despatch it to the laboratory with an appropriately completed request form.

Exercise 4.32 ✎

Exudates are usually present when there is infection or inflammation. Use a sterile swab (wooden stick covered with cotton wool at one end) to collect a sample. Swabs can be taken from the eye, nose, throat, ear, wound, vagina, rectum, or urethra. The dry swab is gently rubbed or rotated against the affected area (and no other), collecting a sample of any exudate (if present) and bacteria. Usually a nasal swab is moistened beforehand with sterile water.

The swab is then immediately placed back into its container which should be clearly labelled and immediately despatched to the laboratory, with an appropriately completed request form.

Testing Specimens

Urinalysis can be defined as the testing of the physical characteristics and composition of freshly voided urine. Use the following procedure:

1. Collect the necessary equipment together—reagent sticks (ensure they have been stored according to the manufacturer's instructions), clean container for collecting the specimen of urine, and a watch with a second hand.

2. Read the instructions that accompany the reagent sticks. They will inform you *when* you need to compare the individual stick patches with the colour chart on the side of the container (after being dipped in urine).

3. Collect a fresh specimen of urine from the client.

4. Dip the reagent stick in the urine, ensuring that all the reagent patches are immersed, whilst ensuring that the fingers holding the stick do not become contaminated with urine.

5. Remove the stick immediately from the urine and tap against the side of the container to remove any excess urine.

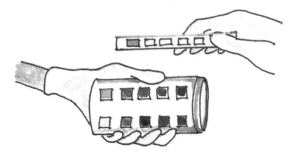

Comparing Patch with Chart

6. Hold the stick at an angle, and wait the required time for each patch before comparing the patch colour against the colour chart.

7. Safely dispose of the urine, used reagent stick, and equipment, ensuring that the remaining reagent sticks are carefully stored away in a locked cupboard.

8. Wash your hands, and then, if necessary, record the results of the urinalysis.

Exercise 4.33 ✎

For **blood sugar analysis** using a glucometer, utilise the following procedure:

1. Collect all necessary equipment—glucometer, tool for pricking the finger (e.g., disposable autolet), testing strips, gloves, tissues, sterile water for cleaning the site to be punctured.

2. Wash your hands using bacteriocidal soap and water or bacteriocidal alcohol rub, and put on the gloves. You may need to explain to the client why you are using gloves.

3. Ask the client which finger he or she would like the sample to be taken from. (Clients can have blood samples taken on several occasions, resulting in some fingers being sore.)

4. Clean the end of the finger with water and a tissue.

When taking a pulse, note the following:

- **Rhythm** (how regular and even the beats are): The pulse rhythm is the sequence of beats. In health, these are regular.

- **Strength** (weak or pounding): The strength or amplitude of the pulse reflects the pulse strength and the elasticity of the arterial wall. The flexibility of the arteries of a young adult feels very different to the hard arteries of an older person suffering from arteriosclerosis.

The two most common points for taking the pulse are the **radial artery** and the **carotid artery**. The wrist is where the radial pulse (from the radial artery) is located. Just follow a line from the base of the thumb, up the inside of the wrist, and the pulse can be easily detected. If it is rather weak, take a reading from the other wrist for comparison.

Exercise 4.43

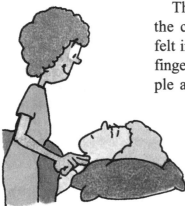

The carotid pulse (from the carotid artery) can be felt in the neck. Slide your fingers from the Adam's apple around the side of the wind pipe. Sometimes a pulse can be detected at the carotid artery when it is too weak to be felt at the wrist.

Other pulse sites include the following:

- Temporal (side of the head)
- Facial (jaw line towards the angle of the jaw)
- Brachial (inside upper arm)
- Femoral (groin)
- Popliteal (behind the knee)
- Dorsalis pedis (instep of foot)
- Posteria tibial (behind the inner ankle)

Exercise 4.44

Follow this procedure for measuring pulse:

1. The pulse should be taken when the person is at rest and relaxed. (Exercise, fever, emotions, or pain, for example, can increase the pulse rate.)

2. Locate the pulse, and press gently against the artery with the middle and index fingers.

3. Using a watch with a second hand, count the beats for a full minute.

4. Record the pulse count on a TPR chart, if required.

5. Report major changes from previous readings to the person-in-charge.

Following are conditions where a client's pulse may need to be regularly and carefully monitored.

- For post-operative and critically ill clients
- During blood transfusions and intravenous infusions
- When clients have severe infections or cardiovascular problems

Exercise 4.45

Monitoring Respirations

The function of the respiratory system is to supply the tissues with oxygen and remove carbon dioxide from the body. Changes in a person's breathing pattern may be a warning sign of respiratory problems. Each respiration (breath) has two parts.

- **Inspiration** (breathing in) is initiated by the contraction of the diaphragm and the muscles of the ribs. The result is that the rib cage rises up and moves out, and the sternum moves forward, increasing the volume of the thorax. This action forces air into the lungs.

- **Expiration** (breathing out) is largely passive, occurring as the respiratory muscles relax and the lungs recoil due to their elastic properties, forcing air out.

To count respirations, watch or feel the person's chest rise and fall. Try to monitor respirations without the person being aware that you are doing it. This can be done by gently resting the back of the hand against the client's chest whilst taking the pulse. It prevents the client from becoming anxious, which is likely to cause a rise in the person's normal rate.

Increased respiration may be due to fever, exercise, stress, disease, or medication. Causes of decreased respiration may include medications and disease.

Pay special attention to the following respirations:

- Very fast or very slow
- Noisy (describe the sound)
- Shallow (very little chest movement)
- Laboured (wheezing with great effort)
- Irregular

Notify the person-in-charge of any irregularities in breathing or major changes from previous readings.

Exercise 4.46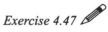

Following are conditions where a client's respirations may need to be regularly and carefully monitored.

- For post-operative and critically ill clients
- When clients have severe infections or cardiovascular problems
- When a client has a chest injury
- For clients who have respiratory problems, such as asthma and bronchitis

Exercise 4.47

The amount of air that is breathed in and out depends on the depth of inspiration and expiration. Information about a person's respiratory efficiency can be achieved by spirometry (measuring various lung capacities).

- **Tidal volume** is the amount of air inhaled and exhaled with each breath when a person is at rest and breathing normally (about 500 ml).

- **Inspiratory reserve volume** is the amount of air that can be inhaled forcibly on top of a tidal volume inspiration (about 3100 ml).

- **Expiratory reserve volume** is the maximum amount of air that can be forcibly breathed out after a normal tidal volume exhalation (about 1200 ml).

- **Residual volume** is the amount of air remaining in the lungs after a forced expiration (about 1200 ml). This prevents the lungs from collapsing completely.

Measuring Peak Flow

Lungs have a remarkable capacity for increasing ventilation, when required (e.g., during exercise, illness, or injury). The *peak flow* is a measure of the tidal volume plus the inspiratory and expiratory reserve volumes. The flow rate is determined both by the diameter of the airways at their narrowest point and by the pressure exerted by the respiratory muscles.

A number of devices are available for measuring peak flow. All have spring-loaded systems that can be deflected by the impact of an individual's expired breath. The devices are relatively inexpensive and easy to use, although they depend on client cooperation in using the maximum respiratory effort whilst ensuring that none of the expired breath is allowed to "leak" outside the peak flow meter mouthpiece.

Clients who have long-standing chest problems like asthma are expected to undertake peak flow measurement on a regular basis. The measurements provide an indication of the effects of treatment or level of deterioration in a respiratory illness.

Exercise 4.48

Measuring Blood Pressure

Blood pressure can be defined as the force exerted by the blood against the walls of the blood vessels. Blood pressure is usually defined in terms of millimetres of mercury (mm Hg). It can fluctuate within a wide range and still be normal.

Average range of blood pressure for adults:

- **Systolic:** 90-140 mm Hg
- **Diastolic:** 60-90 mm Hg

Blood pressure is made up of two measurements (e.g., 120/80). The systolic pressure (the first number) is the maximum pressure of the blood against the walls of the blood vessels following contraction of the ventricles of the heart. The diastolic pressure (second number) is the minimum pressure of the blood against the walls of the blood vessels when the ventricles of the heart are not contracting.

Blood pressure is usually measured for the following reasons:

- To monitor a person's blood pressure over time

- To monitor critically ill, post-operative, and infected clients for shock

- To ensure that there is no circulatory overload for people who are receiving blood transfusions and intravenous infusions

Exercise 4.49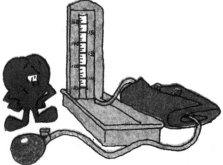

To measure blood pressure, you need a sphygmomanometer and a stethoscope. The ***sphygmomanometer*** consists of a compressions bag enclosed in an unyielding cuff, an inflating bulb (or other device) with a control valve by which the pressure can be increased or decreased to the cuff, and a manometer from which you can read the pressure.

The ***stethoscope*** is simply a bell at the end of a long tube that plugs into your ears so that you can hear the amplified sound. When listening to a blood pressure as it falls from the systolic to the diastolic pressures, a series of five phases of sound can be heard. These are called Korotkoff's sounds, as seen in the diagram below.

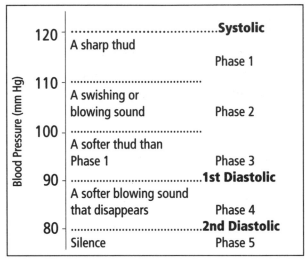

Korotkoff's Sounds

When the cuff pressure has fallen just below the systolic pressure, a clear, but often faint, tapping sound can be heard (phase 1) in conjunction with each cardiac contraction. As the pressure in the cuff is reduced still further, the sound becomes louder before moving on to a swishing or blowing sound (phase 2) and then a soft thud (phase 3). Eventually, the artery is no longer constricted, allowing the blood to flow freely, resulting in a muffled or soft blowing sound (phase 4), before disappearing (phase 5). The diastolic blood pressure is usually defined as the point at which the sound becomes muffled, rather than when the silence occurs.

Exercise 4.50 🖉

Follow these steps for measuring blood pressure:

1. Collect equipment—a sphygmomanometer and a stethoscope.

2. Ensure the client is in the desired position—lying, standing, or sitting with the sphygmomanometer at approximately the same level as the client's heart.

3. Take the arm nearest you, and ensure that you have access to the upper arm by rolling the sleeve up or removing the arm from clothing. Position the arm so that the palm of the hand is facing upwards.

4. Apply the cuff about 2.5 cms above the flexure point on the inside of the arm.

5. Inflate the cuff until the radial pulse can no longer be felt (this is an estimation of the systolic blood pressure). Then deflate the cuff completely, and wait 20 seconds before continuing.

6. Inflate the cuff to a point that is 30 mm Hg higher than the estimated systolic pressure to prevent blood flowing through the artery.

7. Place the bell of the stethoscope over the brachial artery, applying just enough pressure to keep it in place.

8. Slowly deflate the cuff (2-3 mm Hg per second), and make a note of the systolic and diastolic blood pressures. Make sure that you do not deflate it too slowly as this can be uncomfortable for the client. If you do not get an accurate reading on first deflation of the cuff, wait another 20 seconds before attempting another reading of the blood pressure.

9. Where appropriate, document the blood pressure readings. If you think that there are any irregularities, inform the person-in-charge.

10. Safely store away the sphygmomanometer and stethoscope.

The accuracy of blood pressure readings can be improved by using good technique. Ensure that the manometer of the sphymomanometer is kept upright and the hole at the top is patent whilst undertaking the procedure. Make sure that you have the stethoscope over the brachial artery and do not press too hard.

Hypertension is never diagnosed on a single blood pressure reading. There are many reasons why a person's blood pressure might be raised for a short period of time.

Exercise 4.51 🖉

Measuring Weight, Height, and Girth

Changes in weight, height, and girth may indicate health problems. Some people have to be weighed and measured periodically. Accuracy is important. Learn to use the available scales safely and correctly.

The most commonly used scale is the standing balance scale. This type of scale has a measuring rod on which you slide a weight. When the rod is balanced, then you can read the person's weight off the scale. For people who cannot stand, there are bed, wheelchair, and mechanical lift scales.

Follow these guidelines for **weighing** with a standing scale:

1. Explain what you are going to do.

2. Provide privacy.

3. Place both weights at zero with the balance centred.

4. Assist the person onto the scale.

5. Make sure that the person is not holding onto you or the scale.

6. Slide the bottom weight until the balance drops and centres.

7. Chart the weight.

8. Report any unusual findings or observations.

Exercise 4.52 🖉

Guidelines for weighing:

- Weigh at the same time each day.
- Wear the same weight of clothing.
- Weigh with an empty bladder.
- Remove footwear.

Follow these guidelines for **measuring height**:

1. Ask the person to turn away from the scale and stand straight.

2. Slide the measuring rod gently down.

3. Read and record the person's height.

4. If necessary, help the person to get off the scale.

5. Repeat any unusual changes in height to the person-in-charge.

Follow these guidelines for **measuring girth**:

1. Ask the client to stand, or assist the client to a standing position.

2. Take the tape measure and, from the front, pass the tape measure around the back of the client, ensuring that the tape is against the skin and placed around the middle of the client's abdomen. Then take the girth measurement and record it, if necessary.

3. Always measure a person's girth at the same time and in the same way so that there is consistency of measurement.

4. If necessary, help the client back to the chair or into bed, ensuring that he or she is comfortable.

5. Report any unusual changes in girth to the person-in-charge.

Exercise 4.53 🖉

Measuring Fluid Balance

The human body is more than 90 percent water. It constantly loses water and, therefore, must have a constant supply of water to replenish the reservoir.

Water is lost from the body in urine and faeces, in sweat and vomit, and during respiration. Water can be gained by the body naturally in food and drink, and artificially by intravenous infusion.

The body can reduce (but not stop) the amount of water lost by the body when there is a shortage, and increase the excretion of water from the body when the intake is too high. The correct amount of water is needed within the body to maintain the concentration of electrolytes both inside and outside of the billions of cells that make up the human body.

When a person becomes *dehydrated*, you will see the following signs:

- The person feels thirsty.
- The skin becomes dry and inelastic. When it is pinched, it does not quickly regain its shape.
- The mouth will be very dry, and the tongue may be coated.
- The urine becomes very concentrated, and output drops to a minimum.
- The person may become disoriented; and, if the dehydration continues, he or she may die.

Exercise 4.54 🖉

A person can also retain water in the form of *oedema* (tissue swelling). There are a large number of potential causes of oedema, but the following signs are usually present:

- Some part(s) of the body swell because water has been retained.
- There is weight gain.

- In generalised oedema, the water eventually settles (due to gravity) in the lowest parts of the body (e.g., the ankles for a person who is standing, the back and buttocks for someone who is lying in bed).

When monitoring fluid balance, ensure that you measure (or estimate, if necessary) and record all fluids going into a client (e.g., drinks, intravenous fluids, and all fluids that come out of a client—urine, faeces, vomit, drainage from a wound).

To get an accurate **measure of fluid intake**, it is necessary to follow these guidelines:

1. Record all the fluids drank by, or intravenously infused into, a client.

2. Explain to the client what you are doing and why you are doing it, as you will need the client's cooperation to ensure that no fluids are consumed that are not entered onto the fluid balance chart.

3. As well as measuring all fluids taken by mouth, measure foods such as ice cream, jelly, and custard.

4. Record intake as soon as it is consumed.

To get an accurate **measure of fluid output**, it is necessary to follow these guidelines:

1. Record all the fluids that come out of a client. Drainage bottles and the contents of catheter bags are easily measured.

2. Estimate other fluid outputs (e.g., in faeces and when someone has vomited over the floor).

3. Remind the client to tell you when he or she wants to use the toilet.

Report all problems relating to fluid balance measurement to the person-in-charge.

Exercise 4.55

Summary

If you participate in clinical activities, be certain that you understand relevant policies, procedures, and protocol for each activity. Clinical activities vary within different organisations, and this study guide provides only a basic overview. Do not undertake any clinical activities until you have been assessed as being competent.

Check Your Knowledge and Understanding

1. Because of sickness, the department is very short-staffed today. The person-in-charge appears very stressed. She asks you to collect a catheter specimen of urine from one of the clients. You have been present twice when this procedure has been carried out, but have never done it yourself. What should you do?

   a) Say nothing and collect the specimen, hoping that you use the correct procedure.

   b) Apologise to the person-in-charge, and explain that you do not know how to undertake this procedure, and you will be happy to develop the necessary competence at the earliest opportunity.

   c) Apologise to the person-in-charge, and explain that you are willing to "have a go" at the procedure, as long as another staff member is available to supervise you.

   d) Access a copy of the clinical guidelines for this procedure, and read them thoroughly before collecting the specimen.

2. You are changing the dressing on a leg wound for a client who is sat up in bed. During the procedure, as you are cleaning the wound, the client knocks over a glass of water. The water may have splashed onto the sterile field that you have set up on your dressing trolley. What should you do?

   a) Open up a sterile dressing, using a no-touch technique, and gently cover the wound with it. Lightly secure the dressing in place, and ask the client to stay where she is until you return. You then ask a colleague to clear up the spilt water

   whilst you go and set up another dressing trolley so that you can return and complete the procedure.

   b) Temporarily cover the wound with the small sterile paper sheet provided in the dressing pack. Then ask a colleague to clear up the spilt water whilst you go and set up another dressing trolley so that you can return and complete the procedure.

   c) Check the sterile field for splashes and, if you see none, assume the sterile field has not been contaminated and continue with the procedure.

   d) Immediately inform the client that your sterile field may have been contaminated. Ask her to stay where she is and not to touch the wound whilst you clean up the mess, dispose of the old sterile field, and fetch another dressing pack for use on the trolley.

3. You are helping Jim, an elderly gentleman, to maintain his personal hygiene. You have helped him to brush his teeth and have a strip wash at the sink. He has three day's stubble on his chin, but claims that he does not want a shave. He also insists on putting his dirty pyjamas back on as his others are dirty, and he does not like the ones provided by the home. It is obvious that Jim does not want to talk further about the subject. You know that his sister, who has previously complained about the standards of care, is visiting him that evening. What would you do?

a) Accept that Jim has the right to refuse a shave and clean pyjamas. Then plan to intercept Jim's sister before she sees him so that you can inform her of the situation.

b) Try your best to persuade Jim to have a shave and put on some clean pyjamas.

c) Plan to offer Jim counselling so that you can explore why he chooses to remain unshaven and wear dirty pyjamas.

d) Telephone Jim's sister, and ask her to bring in some clean pyjamas for him, mentioning that he is choosing not to shave at the moment.

4. John has had diabetes for many years. At the moment he is recovering from a severe chest infection. He calls you over and points out that one of his big toenails has split and keeps catching on the bed clothes. The nail bed is bleeding slightly. What would you do?

a) Cover the toe and toenail in a non-stick, dry dressing so that it cannot catch the bed clothes, and arrange for him to visit a chiropodist at the earliest opportunity.

b) Carefully cut his toenail, and gently file the edges so that there are no sharp edges to catch the bed clothes.

c) Leave the nail as it is, and introduce a bed cage to his bed to keep the bed clothes off his sore toe.

d) Provide John with a set of nail cutters so that he can trim his own toenail.

5. You are helping a nurse to administer medications to a group of clients. One of the clients, Jill, who is not confused, refuses to take her medication because she says the tablets are making her feel sick. What would you do?

a) Leave Jill's tablets in a small cup at the side of her bed so that she can take them if she feels better later.

b) Accept that Jill has the right to refuse her medication, and hope that she will feel better by the next drugs round so that she can be persuaded to take her medication.

c) Insist that Jill takes her medication, as prescribed by the doctor, as the tablets will "eventually make her feel better."

d) Make a note in the care record that Jill has refused her tablets because she says they are making her sick. Inform the doctor of the situation at the earliest opportunity so that he can consider pre-scribing an alternative medication for Jill.

6. You mention to Jo that you need to take a midstream specimen of her urine. Jo admits that she may have trouble doing this herself as she has arthritis. After ensuring that Jo has carefully cleaned around the labia and urethra, what would you do?

a) Allow Jo to pass urine into a clean bed-pan, and take the sample from there.

b) Sit Jo on a commode in one of the toilet cubicles, place a sterile jug under her, and quickly collect the first sample of urine that she passes so that you can then leave her in peace to finish her toiletting.

c) Sit Jo on a commode in one of the toilet cubicles. Allow her to pass urine into the toilet for a few seconds, and then place a sterile jug under the commode in order to collect a sample of her urine. Then leave her in peace to finish her toiletting.

d) Insist that Jo attempts to collect the sample herself in a sterile jug.

7. You have taken John's blood pressure and find that it is 160/110, much higher than one would expect for a fit 40 year old. What should you do?

   a) Immediately inform the person-in-charge about John's hypertension.

   b) Ask a couple of colleagues to take John's blood pressure to check that your reading is correct.

   c) Ask John to lie down and relax for an hour, and then return and retake the blood pressure.

   d) Check his blood pressure chart to compare the current blood pressure against the others that have been charted. If it is significantly different from his usual blood pressure, ask John if there is any reason why his blood pressure should be raised. If there is no obvious reason for the raised blood pressure, inform the person-in-charge.

Module 5

Working Within a Team

Be an effective member of the care team.

Need-to-know words:

- critical incident
- eureka feeling
- hypochondriac
- learning style
- mentor
- reflection
- service specification

Objectives:

- Demonstrate how to work effectively within a team.
- Describe how management and leadership skills can be utilised within teams.
- Outline how personal power strategies can improve personal effectiveness.
- Utilise personal development opportunities whilst working within a team.
- Describe how lifelong learning improves personal effectiveness.
- Reflect on your practice.
- Highlight the importance of assessing client needs.
- Describe how care programmes should be planned and reviewed.

Module 5 Introduction

Module 5 relates to three units of the level 3 NVQ/SVQ Award in Care:

Unit CU9: **Contribute to the development and effectiveness of work teams** is an option group B unit. It consists of three elements of competence:

- CU9.1 Contribute to effective team practice

- CU9.2 Contribute to the development of others in the work team

- CU9.3 Develop oneself in own work role

Unit CU7: **Develop one's own knowledge and practice** is a mandatory group A unit. It consists of two elements of competence:

- CU7.1 Reflect on and evaluate one's own values, priorities, interests and effectiveness

- CU7.2 Synthesise new knowledge into the development of one's own practice

Unit SC8: **Contribute to the development, provision and review of care programmes** is an option group B unit. It consists of four elements of competence:

- SC8.1 Obtain information about clients and their needs of the service

- SC8.2 Contribute to planning how client's needs can best be met

- SC8.3 Agree on services to be provided to meet clients' needs

- SC8.4 Contribute to reviewing the effectiveness of care programmes

Part 1: Working Effectively Within Teams (CU9)

Ensure that environments are prepared for clinical activities.

One definition of a team is that it is "a group of people working together to achieve an identified result." Some people work in stable teams where the membership changes very little over the years. Others work with an ever-changing team, either because of shift systems or because there is a high turnover of staff.

The majority of teams work as part of a larger organisation. A larger organisation usually has a statement that states clearly what it is trying to achieve. This is usually called a mission statement, although it can also be referred to as a vision statement, a philosophy statement, or a statement of values. It is often printed on headed stationary and posted on office and corridor walls.

Exercise 5.1 🖊

Your team may consist of team members who are employed entirely by one organisation, or the team may consist of individuals who are employed by a number of care organisations from the public, private, and voluntary sectors. Even if the team are all employed by the one organisation, it is highly likely that you will have to manage relationships with a number of other departments within the organisation.

Exercise 5.2 🖊

Team effectiveness depends on the following team characteristics:

- Cooperation, trust, and respect between team members

- Good, open, and honest communication networks within the team

- Individuals taking personal responsibility for the work that needs to be done

- Work in progress being accurately and clearly documented and available to all

- The setting of clear standards of performance and targets

- Commitment of all team members to provide mutual support and achieve performance standards and targets

- A sense of "belonging" and commitment to the team

- Team members having the appropriate skills and knowledge for their roles

- A good balance of strengths and weaknesses within the team

- Individuals feeling comfortable in asking for help when they need it and in refusing demands that are unreasonable

- All team members being encouraged to participate in decision making, especially in relation to change

Exercise 5.3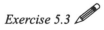

When a group of people are expected to work together, the following team problems can occur for a variety of reasons.

- **Avoidance** happens when there is interpersonal conflict within the team or when the team is struggling to cope. Team members avoid each other, and there is a tendency for sickness rates to increase.

- **Closed shop** happens when the team leader and team are very supportive of each other and defend one another. Conflict within the team is "papered over," and new initiatives tend to be sabotaged. Pressures for change from outside the team are ignored.

- **Funeral parlour** happens when the team members reminisce over the past good times (e.g., good team leader, enjoyable work). This results in team members focusing on depression and conflict, rather than on being effective.

- **Gossip mongering** happens when the team members spend a lot of time in team meetings gossiping and joking, rather than getting on with the business.

- **Mutiny** happens when the team as a whole feel that they are being treated unfairly by the team leader or manager. He or she is ostracised, and the team focuses more on making life difficult for the manager, rather than on trying to make the system work.

- **Skeleton in the cupboard** happens when there is a "secret" that only a few team members know about (e.g., the personal problems of a team member). Discussions are steered away from the topic during meetings, leaving everybody feeling uncomfortable.

- **Strangers** happens when the team members don't know each other very well, and there is a lack of assertiveness and leadership within the team. Any suggestion is grabbed and accepted as a solution because there is very little innovation, and people are scared to disagree. Team members have very little to say to each other outside the meetings.

- **Victimisation** happens when a single person or small number of people are blamed for everything. The victim is often someone who challenges the system, but does not have the assertiveness skills to stop him/herself from being "bullied."

There are a number of factors that can influence **team effectiveness** as shown in the illustration below:

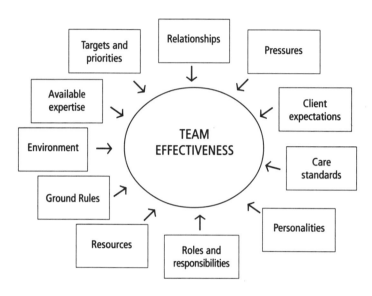

Factors that Affect Team Effectiveness

Exercise 5.4 🖉

A team can perform a number of valuable functions for individual team members. Following are examples:

- Clarification of team goals and targets
- Negotiation of individual roles within the team
- Integration of team members' expertise to enable client needs to be met
- Motivation, support, and encouragement
- Reductions in stress levels
- Encouragement of personal development and learning "on the job"

Leadership

Leadership behaviour is not the prerogative of the team leader. All members of a team display some leadership behaviours. There are two main types of leadership behaviour—task-focused behaviours and group-focused behaviours.

Task-Focused Leadership Behaviours:

- Offer facts, give opinions and ideas, provide suggestions and relevant information
- Propose goals, targets, and tasks to be completed.
- Provide direction for the team by helping to plan teamwork and focusing team members' attention on the task in hand.
- Pull together related ideas or suggestions made by the team in order to summarise the major points.
- Outline team standards and norms in order to ensure that team members are aware of the direction that they are working in and the progress made.
- Assess how practical and workable different ideas are.

Group-Focused Leadership Behaviours:

- Warmly encourage all members of the team to participate and to remain open to the ideas of others.
- Relieve tension and increase the enjoyment of team participation by joking and having fun.
- Ask team members how they feel about the way the group is working.
- Help energise the group by stimulating group members to produce high quality work.
- Promote open discussion of conflict between team members to resolve disagreements and increase group cohesiveness.
- Listen and serve as an interested member of the audience for other group members.

Exercise 5.5 🖉

A good team will have an appropriate balance of team members—some who use mostly task-focused leadership behaviours and some who use mostly group-focused leadership behaviours.

Management Style

The management style of the team leader can have a significant effect on the effectiveness of the team. There are three main management styles—traditional, human relations, and human resources.

The **traditional** style assumes that people have a tendency to be lazy and cannot be trusted to do a good job. This is based on the assumption that the things that individuals would like to do are not the same as those wanted in the job, and they should be tightly controlled to make sure they work towards organisational goals. In this model, a large number of management policies are written which prescribe close supervision and tight control of team members performing narrowly defined jobs. This is acceptable because the organisation is buying the services and obedience of the employee in order to achieve its goals.

The **human relations** style allows a limited amount of team-member participation in decision making and self-control. This is based on the assumption that people are essentially loyal and dependable if their basic social needs are fulfilled within the job. That is, they feel that they are important to the organisation and that their work is recognised by the team leader. The model presumes that team members' limited power base will improve their morale and personal satisfac-

tion. Therefore, they will be more willing to cooperate with the direction given by the team leader.

Exercise 5.6

The **human resources** style allows for a continually expanding degree of team participation, self-direction, and self-control. This is based on the assumption that the creative abilities of most team members are often under-utilised. Also, most team members will exercise responsibility and self-direction in the achievement of goals that they have established. This style of management accepts that the quality of decision making is improved when the decisions are made by the people who know the job best —the team members. This model produces the highest level of satisfaction at work because of the opportunities for recognition and personal achievement.

Personal Power

There are a number of things that you can do to build up your personal power base and effectiveness, both within the team and the organisation as a whole (Marquis & Huston - 1996).

Expand your personal resources. Self-awareness, vitality, resilience, mental and emotional strength, are all characteristics of the powerful person. Therefore, improving your abilities in any of these areas will increase your personal power. Likewise, maintaining a healthy mind and body through exercise and good nutrition are simple but often overlooked ways of increasing personal power.

Present a powerful picture to others. How you look, act, and speak influences whether others view you as powerful or powerless. The care worker who stands tall, and is poised, assertive, articulate, and well-groomed presents a picture to others of personal control and power. Team members who stand out are those who do more, work harder, and contribute to the organisation. Neither "clock watchers" nor "nine-to-fivers," they attend meetings, attend in-service training, and accept their share of the unpopular jobs, shifts, and holiday allocations without complaining.

Identify the powerful in the organisation. It is important for individuals to be aware of their own limitations and to seek help. Help should be sought from the powerful individuals within the team and the wider organisation.

Learn the language and symbols of the organisation. Each organisation has its own culture, as well as its own values. It is necessary for new team members to understand this culture and to be socialised into the organisation if they are to build a power base. There are certain "taboos" that exist in each organisation, and being unaware of what they are can result in embarrassment.

Learn how to use the organisation's priorities. Teams and organisations tend to have priority lists of goals they wish to achieve. Individuals seeking to construct a power base must be aware of these goals and priorities and use this knowledge when meeting their own needs.

Increase your professional skills and knowledge. Because it is expected that team members will perform their jobs well, your job performance must be excellent to enhance personal power. One method of achieving this is by increasing your professional skills and knowledge until an advanced level of expertise is reached. Having knowledge and skills that others lack, greatly enhances your power base.

Maintain a broad vision. Team members can develop a narrow view of the total organisation. Power builders always look upward and outward. The successful team member not only recognises how the care team fits in with the larger organisation, but also how the organisation as a whole fits into the scheme of the entire community.

Use experts and seek counsel. New team members should seek out role models to emulate. By soliciting the advice and counsel of others, new team members demonstrate their willingness to be team players, that they are cautious and welcome advice from others, and that they are not brash newcomers who think they have all the answers.

Be flexible. An individual wishing to acquire power should develop a reputation as someone who can compromise. The rigid, uncompromising team member is viewed as insensitive to the needs of the team.

Learn to toot your own horn. There is an art to accepting compliments. One should be gracious, but certainly not passive, when praise is given for your good work. Your good practice can be used as an example to improve team performance.

Maintain a sense of humour. Appropriate humour is a very powerful tool, and the ability to laugh at oneself and not take oneself too seriously is one of the most important power builders.

Empower others. Care workers can empower each other by sharing knowledge, maintaining cohesiveness, valuing the work that is done, and supporting each other. You will increase your own personal power when you empower others.

Exercise 5.7 🖉

Conflict Resolution

Conflict can be defined as incompatible behaviour between one or more people who have different goals. Whenever two or more people are brought together, the stage is set for potential conflict.

Conflict is unhealthy when it is avoided, passively accepted, or approached on a win-lose basis (one party wins, the others lose). In these situations, there is likely to be animosity where communications break down, trust and mutual support deteriorate, and hostilities result. This results in poor quality work where the damage to relationships can be very difficult to repair. The drawbacks of this type of conflict include the following:

· Poor motivation at work leading to absenteeism, sabotage, time wasting, poor quality of work

· High levels of stress

· A decline in interpersonal communications

- The organisation is diverted away from its major goals.

- The external image of the organisation may suffer.

Conflict is natural and healthy when it causes the parties to explore new ideas, test their values and beliefs, and stretch their imaginations. Used constructively, conflict can stimulate great creativity which leads to a wider choice of actions, better interpersonal relationships, and better results.

The benefits of positively handled conflict include the following:

- It brings about role and goal clarification and team development.

- Information is mobilised and released, leading to better communication.

- Quality of decisions is improved.

- Increased energy levels lead to innovation and change.

- It brings like-minded people together to pursue shared interests.

- It can provide an impetus for team stability.

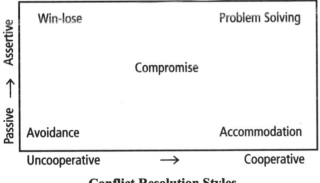

Conflict Resolution Styles

There are five styles of conflict resolution highlighted in the above diagram:

- **Avoidance** occurs when an individual is neither assertive nor cooperative. This is the least effective style of conflict resolution.

- **Win-lose** occurs when an individual is assertive, but uncooperative.

- **Accommodation** occurs when an individual is cooperative, but not assertive.

- **Compromise** occurs when an individual is averagely assertive and cooperative.

- **Problem-solving** occurs when an individual is very assertive and very cooperative. This is the most effective style of conflict resolution.

Exercise 5.8

Following are important points to remember regarding conflict resolution:

- Abusive, aggressive, bullying, and discriminatory remarks made by team members are unacceptable and should be openly challenged.

- Occasionally a team issue (e.g., stress levels, sickness rates, bullying, harassment) cannot be resolved, and it may be necessary to pass it on to someone who has the authority and capability to reach a resolution.

- There is a difference between work relationships and personal relationships. You cannot be expected to enjoy the company of every member of your team, but you are expected to develop a positive working relationship with all your colleagues.

Personal Development within Teams

Most organisations are under constant pressure to become more efficient and improve their performance. Managers are asked to get more out of limited resources. An organisation's performance depends directly on the performance of its employees.

The ultimate goal of any organisation is to become a **self-learning organisation**. The health and social care sectors are constantly changing. A self-learning organisation is one that has effectively developed the capacity for continuous learning and adaptation which includes the following characteristics:

- Encourages learning by all employees
- Places only partial emphasis on formal training
- Places high emphasis on learning from experience and personal development
- Has the ability to continuously change as required

Organisations that aspire towards a high performance culture will do the following:

- Be clear about their targets and standards of performance.
- Ensure continuous assessment of performance and feedback.
- Provide recognition for outstanding performance.

Exercise 5.9

In a learning organisation, it is essential that all employees get regular feedback about their work performance. To formalise the feedback process, most organisations have developed a system of performance appraisal or review so that employees can receive feedback from their line managers.

Benefits of performance appraisal:

- The appraisal clarifies the individual's strengths and weaknesses.
- It usually involves the negotiation of a set of personal objectives or goals for the year and an agreed plan of action to achieve them. The objectives should be achievable, realistic, relatively challenging, and related to service delivery. You will then know what is expected of you, and you can direct your energies accordingly.
- Your progress toward achieving those objectives should be monitored and periodically reviewed with your team leader; and, if necessary, the objectives can be re-negotiated.
- When you know what you are expected to achieve, you can better evaluate your own performance, and your team leader can more easily provide feedback on your performance.
- In addition to focusing on work targets, a performance appraisal should encourage you to take responsibility for your own development, learning, and performance. This can be achieved by setting one or more personal development targets within the objectives. There should be a balance, though, between the individual's personal development needs and the demands of the work role.
- Another focus can be career counselling and support for promotion.
- The identification and clarification of work performance problems can lead to better understanding of expectations. If a team leader is unhappy with your performance, you can both negotiate a plan to improve your effectiveness.

Drawbacks of performance appraisal:

- It can be difficult for performance appraisal to take account of teamwork because it usually focuses on the work of individuals.
- There is always room for disagreement concerning quality of work performance, level of support provided, and appropriateness of objectives. This is especially likely to happen if you and your team leader dislike each other, and you suspect that your work performance is being unfairly appraised.

Exercise 5.10

In addition to your performance appraisal, ask other members of the care team for feedback (peer review) on specific areas of performance. Any feedback should be evaluated objectively and constructively so that it can be used to improve your future work performance. When there is conflict within the care team, though, it can be difficult to give and accept feedback.

Team meetings are another important way of developing the care team. Meetings should be well-structured, organised, and documented. They should focus on relevant issues, encourage all to attend and participate, and should not be seen as a waste of time and effort. The potential benefits of team meetings include the following:

- Opportunities for dissemination of information to the team

- Opportunities to organise and coordinate the delivery of care

- Discussions about conflict and controversy (e.g., high sickness rates, tensions between staff members, complaints from outside)

- Strategic planning for the team's future (e.g., decisions on the use of resources, timetabling, allocation of staff development monies)

- Feedback to the team on the team's performance, using information gained from the team's or organisation's quality assurance system

Exercise 5.11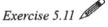

When providing feedback to junior care workers on their performance, it is important that both you and your colleague feel able to talk freely. This is achieved by using a counselling-type approach that follows these guidelines:

- **Be descriptive, rather than judgmental:**

Descriptive: "Please explain what caused the accident."

Judgmental: "How did you manage to do such a stupid thing?"

- **Be supportive, not authoritarian:**

Supportive: "What do you think we ought to do in this case?"

Authoritarian: "This is what you are going to have to do in this case."

- **Reflect equality, rather than superiority.**

Equality: "Although we've done it this way for years, do you have any ideas on how we might do it better?"

Superiority: "I've been doing it this way successfully for donkey's years."

- **Be flexible, not opinionated.**

Flexible: "This appears to be the best way of doing it. Do you know of any other possibilities?"

Opinionated: "This is the best way of doing it."

Following are other factors to help with the development of others in the work team:

- Remember to offer praise and positive feedback to colleagues when they are merited.

- Offer information and advice in a manner which is constructive. Show sensitivity to the individual's needs and concerns, and take account of the overall situation. Modify language, where appropriate, to ensure understanding. Be aware of situations when your advice would not be accepted.

- Be open and honest when a member is in need of support and/or needs to be monitored (e.g., following a family bereavement, after making a number of medication errors). The planned interventions should be appropriate for the individual concerned, his/her role, and the timing and location of activities.

- Offer appropriate support and encouragement when colleagues are undertaking new or difficult tasks.

- Step in when a colleague appears to be in difficulties or is about to make a mistake. You need to take account of the person's role, status within the organisation, and any other constraints (e.g., the presence of a client's family).

- Others can benefit from your knowledge and experience. If you have information that would be of benefit to others, put it together in an appropriate format, and disseminate it through the most effective channels.

Exercise 5.12 ✎

When you have information that is required by a colleague occupying a more senior position within the team or organisation, you may need to modify your approach according to your position. This is especially true if there is potential controversy within the information that you want to pass on. The best way of knowing how to interact with these people is to watch how others do it, and then adapt their approach to your situation and status.

On occasion, a senior colleague may not like the information that you are passing on. To do this successfully, you will need to get the right mix between being assertive, sensitive, and showing respect to the person's position in the organisation.

Part 2: Developing Lifelong Learning (CU7)

Participate in the lifelong development of your own knowledge and learning.

This section should be of particular interest to all health and social care workers who are accountable for their own actions and have a responsibility for their own personal development. Your personal priorities for the present and the future can have a significant effect on the actions you take in terms of developing your own knowledge and competence.

Exercise 5.13 ✎

Health and social care organisations are continually having to change due to market forces and government legislation. Following are various causes of organisational change.

Internal Forces for Change:

- Policies/procedures/regulations

- Health and safety issues

- People's expectations of the availability and quality of care

- Attitudes (e.g., to health and welfare)

- Culture (organisational and local)

- Prevailing management style utilised within your organisation

- Modernisation and equipment changes

- Availability of funds within the organisation

- Introduction of new concepts, models, theories, or approaches to working

- Local strategies and policies

External Forces for Change:

- Changes in health and social care markets

- New technologies that become available (e.g., information technology)

- Clients' preferences and choices for health and social care

- Competitors from the public, private, and voluntary sectors of the market

- Financial incentives for organisations to change

- Government financial and social policies

- New legislation relating to health and social care.

Exercise 5.14 ✎

The only way you can keep abreast of developments and ensure that you are up-to-date in your chosen area of practice is by developing the skills of lifelong learning. You need to develop and maintain your competence so that you can provide high quality care whilst ensuring that the chances of making a mistake are minimised. The problem is that you have to balance your personal development needs against a number of other responsibilities which make demands on your time (e.g., workload, family, personal life).

Lifelong learning does not mean that you should always be attending courses of study and collecting educational certificates. Alternatively, you should always be on the lookout for opportunities to learn from your work and life experiences. There are a number of ways you can do this. Following are examples:

- Planning personal development activities
- Reading relevant books, journals, and magazines
- Reflecting on your practice (e.g., critical incidents)
- Taking an active part in team meetings
- Preparing an up-to-date learning resource on a specific area of practice

Any aspect of your work can be used for personal development purposes. It only requires you to reflect and make a few notes. Consider the following:

- You have experienced something new.
- You make a mistake that you would like to avoid making in the future.
- You are contemplating doing something different.
- You notice that your own values, attitudes, or priorities may be changing or are affecting your work.
- You need to evaluate the effectiveness of your own work or the work of others.

The whole process can be enhanced if you do it in conjunction with others. This can happen in the supportive environment of a team meeting, or it can occur on a one-to-one basis with an experienced colleague who is willing to act as your mentor. Whether you do this by yourself or with others, you need to give it the necessary time and effort. You also need to structure the known facts and your thoughts, and feel mentally and physically comfortable with the process.

Exercise 5.15 🖉

Self and Environmental Assessment

It is always worthwhile completing a self and environmental assessment in relation to the key areas of your work. (Some NVQ/SVQ candidates are encouraged to carry out a similar exercise to identify their prior learning against the components of their award). Basically, the self and environmental assessment is a form of self-assessment. In the strengths and weaknesses, you are expected to identify personal factors (internal to you) that are likely to affect your ability to demonstrate competence in the key areas of your work.

Strengths: Identify skills, abilities, knowledge, attitudes, and values that you have that are relevant to the key areas. This can include learning outcomes achieved at courses and study days previously undertaken, and learning achieved from your work and life experiences. It also includes those aspects of your work that you enjoy doing.

Weaknesses: Identify aspects of the key areas of your work that you feel you cannot do very well, do not know much about, or may find particularly difficult to understand. It also includes those aspects of your work that you do not particularly enjoy and any values or attitudes you hold that are not compatible with your work roles (e.g., you have always been scared of clients who have a mental illness, you are prejudiced against people who are hypochondriacs).

The opportunities and barriers allow you to identify those factors in the environment (external to you) that are likely to affect your ability to achieve personal development in the key areas of your work.

Opportunities: Identify those aspects of your work and personal life that are likely to help you, or make things easier for you, to achieve personal development in the key areas of your work (e.g., nearby health studies library, an existing personal development plan agreed as part of your performance appraisal, study leave is available, a senior colleague is happy to act as your mentor, your mother is happy to look after the kids whilst you study, good learning resources are available at your place of work).

Barriers: Identify those aspects of your work and personal life that may have an adverse affect, or make things difficult for you, to achieve personal development in the key areas of your work (e.g., home life is making it difficult to study, personal development is not seen as being important within your team, you are expected to achieve paper qualifications rather than develop your competence, you do not have good library and study skills). It can also include areas of your work which are likely to change or come under threat in the near future.

Self-assessment helps you in the following areas:

· Developing self-awareness in relation to your strengths and weaknesses

· Creating an awareness of the opportunities and barriers that are available for personal development

· Using information to plan and prioritise your future personal development

Exercise 5.16 🖉

Reflecting on Practice

Fundamental to the process of reflecting on practice is the belief that care workers are adult learners. Adults have a deep need to be self-directing and independent. They are motivated to learn as they experience needs that learning will satisfy. Their orientation to learning is life-centred, and experience is viewed as the richest source of learning.

This philosophy of learning seeks to harness the experience of practitioners within the learning process.

It encourages the identification of experiences as a resource for learning, and it assists practitioners in developing self-directed approaches to their personal development for the purposes of improving the quality of their practice.

It is generally accepted that adult learners utilise an experiential learning cycle, whether or not they know they are doing so. This model of learning highlights how people have experiences on which they can reflect. The learning that is identified in the reflections can then be conceptually fitted in with that individual's current knowledge which is related to that subject area. If that learning is to be useful, it should be utilised in practice (sometimes called action learning). This then creates new experiences which can be reflected on, and so you start a new experiential cycle.

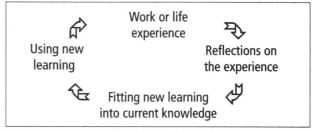

Experiential Learning Cycle

The art of reflection is taken from the experiential learning cycle. In the fields of health and social care, reflection is viewed as a conscious process of thinking about, and interpreting, personal experiences in order to learn from them. Therefore, reflecting on practice is a very personal process, although it can be shared with others. Most people think back to a personal experience and try to work out why something happened, or wonder what would have happened if they had done something different. This is the art of reflection.

The process of structuring your thoughts and writing them down on paper means that you can keep them for future reference and learn from your experiences. A care worker may have 15 years of valuable experience (or, without reflection, may have one year's experience repeated 15 times). Reflection turns experience into learning which, where appropriate, should lead to improvements in your practice.

Reflections are usually based on significant life and work experiences:

- Aspects of daily routine that are usually given very little thought, but for which personal strengths and weaknesses in that area have a significant effect on the quality of care/service delivered

- Individual critical incidents (e.g., a difficult and/or important situation which is memorable because it was handled particularly well or badly)

- Ongoing positive or negative situations (e.g., having to cope with a difficult manager)

- Experiences in personal life that had an effect on your work (e.g., a bereaved relative that did/did not receive the most appropriate support from health and social care professionals)

- The limits of your own work role and its inter-relationship with the work roles of others

Exercise 5.17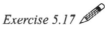

The process of writing reflections often helps to confirm existing care skills, knowledge, and attitudes. It enables you to identify your personal abilities and appreciate your own practice so that your personal achievements can be evaluated and/or discussed with others. Eventually, when you feel comfortable in reflecting on your practice, it becomes less important to collect certificates of attendance at courses, workshops, study days, and conferences because certificates do not provide evidence of learning.

It is much more satisfying to reflect on what has been learned from your learning experiences by identifying learning outcomes and outlining how the new learning has influenced your practice. At a later date, when this new learning has been implemented in practice, its effect should be evaluated. This is the foundation for reflecting on practice. Reflecting on your practice is not easy at first. However, it does become easier and more enjoyable with practice.

A reflective write-up should include all or most of the following components (Boud et al., 1985):

1. **Return to the Experience**

   A clear, concise and accurate description of the event(s), highlighting the following:

   - Significant background/historical factors
   - The place and the people involved and their roles
   - The events as they unfolded
   - Any consequences of the event

   If appropriate, evaluate your own performance (including existing knowledge) and the performance of others within the event.

2. **Attend to Feelings**

   Outline your thoughts, feelings, and emotions concerned with the event. (If you are still trying to come to terms with your emotions, then you are not yet ready to articulate and learn from it.) There are two types of feelings:

   - *Positive feelings*—sense of achievement, happiness, relief, "eureka" feeling, etc.

   - *Negative feelings*—hurt, uncertainty, embarrassment. These can form a barrier that prevents learning from the experience.

3. **Re-evaluate the experience**

   When feelings have been dealt with, then a practitioner can stand back and re-evaluate the experience as an objective observer:

   - Evaluate the outcomes of the event (challenging any previous assumptions that may have been made). Were they good, bad, significant? If so, why, and for whom?

   - What has been learned from this experience? (Make sense of the learning by interpreting, analysing, and evaluating it. This enables an assessment of the value of what is known and what needs to be known.)

119

- How does the learning relate to your existing knowledge and skills?

- Are there any knowledge or skills deficits identified?

- How is the learning to be incorporated into practice?

Exercise 5.18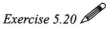

Learning Styles

Everyone has personal preferences for how they like to learn. Some people like to sit in classrooms and listen to lectures, whilst others like different kinds of learning (e.g., watching videos, using distance learning materials, using computer-based learning, learning on the job). People tend to learn best from learning experiences that fit their personal learning style.

Whatever the preferred learning style, the experiential learning cycle is relevant. Reflect on the experience, and identify what has been learned. Fit that learning into current knowledge. Then try out the new learning in practice, which leads to a new experience that can be reflected on.

Using the experiential learning cycle, you do not always learn what you intended to learn from a learning experience. That is, there are sometimes unintentional and unexpected learning outcomes (e.g., learning about how colleagues cope with the pressure of the job, discovering the learning preferences of others, being able to compare your own abilities to those of others, learning during the coffee break about planned management changes).

Exercise 5.19

Part 3:   Contributing to Care Planning   (SC8)

Contribute effectively to the development and review of care plans.

This section is relevant to any care worker who has a role in contributing to the assessment of client needs and the development, provision, and review of programmes of care to meet those needs. Usually the qualified, health or social care professional retains accountability for these activities.

Exercise 5.20

The whole process of care planning must be client-centred. Follow these general guidelines when contributing to care planning:

- The planned care must meet an individual client's assessed needs, rather than the care service's needs.

- The client and, where appropriate, family and friends, are equal partners in the care planning process. Therefore, they should all be encouraged and supported to participate in the process of assessing, planning, and evaluating care, especially when they are feeling powerless and vulnerable.

- Show that you have the client's interests at heart, whatever the person's chosen lifestyle, economic status, or cultural and religious beliefs might be.

- Your focus should be on fostering the client's personal development, growth, and independence.

- If necessary, an advocate can be appointed for the client.

- Your role in relation to a specific client should be agreed in relation to all who are involved in assessing needs and planning care, especially if you are to be the designated point of contact for the client.

- Great efforts should be made on developing a good relationship based on trust, where possible, with the client, the family, and others who have an interest in the client's well-being.

- Clients should be encouraged and enabled to express their fears, needs, preferences, beliefs, opinions, interests, and to ask questions throughout the care planning process. If necessary, an interpreter should be arranged.

- Discussions and negotiations should ensure that everyone present can understand what is being said (e.g., jargon and abbreviations are avoided, pace and level of information are carefully controlled).

- Clients should be involved in deciding who is going to contribute to the care planning process.

- Accurate records of all decisions made and services provided must be clearly and neatly documented and copies provided for all relevant people.

A client can be an individual person or a whole family. When the client is a family, the number of interacting persons increases the complexity of the situation. The Carers (Recognition and Services) Act (1995) highlights how carers have the right to have their needs assessed if they are adults caring for an elderly or disabled person, young carers who are under the age of 18 years, or carers of children with special needs.

Groups who are not entitled to a carer assessment are people employed to provide care, volunteer carers, and non-substantial or non-regular carers.

For the care planning process and subsequent management of care, it is essential that you develop an effective working relationship based on openness and trust with the client. This can only be achieved by freeing up uninterrupted time to meet with, and talk to, the client and his or her family, and employing a counselling-type approach.

Exercise 5.21 🖉

Assessing Clients' Needs

Assessment is the act of collecting information about and reviewing a human situation for the purposes of identifying actual or potential client needs and problems. There is a wide variety of potential client needs that can be categorised under one or more of the following headings:

· Advocacy	· Cultural	· Educational
· Emotional	· Employment	· Financial
· Legal	· Physical	· Psychological
· Recreational	· Social	· Spiritual

Usually, a first step is to assess whether a client is having his or her basic human needs met.

Basic **physical** needs:

- A bed and a room: Ensure that a person feels safe.

- Food: Allow the client to choose foods and, where possible, cook for him/herself.

- Clothing: Provide the opportunity to choose the clothing that is to be worn and the chance to purchase one's own clothing.

- Shelter and heating: Ensure that the environment can be controlled.

- Safety and well-being: Provide maximum safety that allows acceptable risk-taking and access to appropriate health services (e.g., chiropodist) and local facilities (e.g., hairdresser).

Basic **psychological** needs:

- Security in relation to keeping a home: Clients' needs do change, especially those who are vulnerable. It can be quite difficult to promise that a person can stay at, or access, a chosen home.

- Significant personal relationships: Although it is accepted that a client's family have a duty to take an interest in, or provide care for, a relative, there are a significant number of people who have no one they can depend on.

- Privacy: Respect the need for privacy and to be able to choose the people one would like to live among.

Basic **societal** needs:

- Access to money: This can be important for self-confidence as well as the need to be able to buy things and pay bills.

- Opportunities to socialise: Prevent isolation from occurring, although there may be risks involved.

- Daytime occupation: A job or work placement or a place at a day centre provides clients with the chance to mingle with others, meet people, and prevent boredom.

- Shopping: This is an important part of everyday life, even if help in terms of transport and escort is needed.

- Pastimes, sports, and hobbies: Promote activities so that the client can take part in a range of interests.

- Holidays: These can give a break to relatives and carers as well as the client.

- Further education: Learning offers life-enhancing opportunities to clients.

Exercise 5.22 ✎

You need to be aware that there are some circumstances in which the timing and format of assessment is prescribed by legislation and local policy. Following are examples of circumstances:

- When a client moves on from special school, he or she will require a future needs assessment.

- When a client who has a disability leaves school, he or she should be assessed according to the procedures laid down by the Disabled Persons (Services Consultation and Representation) Act (1986).

- When a client is preparing for a move of home, he or she can request a community care assessment.

- When a client has been receiving services for a while, the whole situation should be reviewed at regular intervals .

- When a child is being considered for adoption, assessment is required.

A client's needs may differ from time to time and can be influenced by what the client views as stressful and "normal." All possible sources of information should be identified and assessed (e.g., client, client's partner, relatives, friends, agencies involved in providing services, those who have a rightful say in the services to be offered such as courts, purchasing organisation via service specifications).

Usually the first task in identifying needs is to make an initial assessment. An assessment instrument may be provided by your organisation to structure this part of the assessment. A time and a place for taking the history should be specified. This can be at a clinic, a client's home, a hospital, a doctor's surgery, drug rehabilitation centre, remand home, etc.

Exercise 5.23 ✎

Be flexible in collecting information for the history so that you are meeting the client's needs, rather than simply following the format of the form. Whilst taking the history, take the opportunity to focus on specific areas of interest, and check for accuracy and validity of data as the interview develops. The time spent in making an accurate initial assessment is time well spent as it can save a lot of time later by preventing mistakes and the wasteful use of resources.

Usually an assessment is initiated by asking the client starter questions. These are open questions that invite broad answers from which additional questions can be developed. Following are examples of starter questions:

- "Describe how your problems affect your personal life. How do you feel about this?"
- "Would you describe yourself as an independent person? Please explain." (rather than asking, "What is your problem?").
- "What can you do for yourself?"

After the initial assessment/history has been taken and initial problems identified, specific assessments can be carried out by appropriately qualified and experienced people (e.g., financial assessment by welfare benefits officer, care placement assessment by a care manager). Inconsistencies and gaps in information should be clarified, if possible.

Exercise 5.24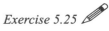

In order to obtain all the necessary information relating to clients and their needs, clearly explain the assessment and care planning process to the client. Encourage clients to decide, where possible, who they want to be included in the assessment and care planning process.

Use all your senses in collecting data (e.g., smell for alcohol or tobacco on the breath, incontinence, or lack of personal hygiene; sight for needle tracks on the arms or appropriateness of dress; touch to feel temperature or muscle tension; hearing to pinpoint accent and culture, problems with respiration).

Provide reasons for asking detailed questions about "delicate" subject areas (e.g., personal finances, continence problems). Ensure that when you put forward your views about a subject, they are offered in a non-threatening way which acknowledges the client's viewpoint.

Outline where all the relevant information is stored and who will have access to it. Promise that confidentiality will be preserved unless, because of legal guidelines or local policies, information has to be passed on to other authorities (e.g., when someone admits to abusing a child or is claiming welfare benefits to which they are not entitled).

A good way of prioritising client needs is to use Maslow's Hierarchy of Needs. This model assumes that the needs nearest the base of the pyramid are the most important and need to be satisfied first, before subsequent needs are tackled (e.g., a client's needs for acceptance would not be important if his physiological and safety needs were not being met).

Maslow's Hierarchy of Needs

- **Self-actualisation needs:** to develop to the fullest potential, to become the best person possible, with the fullest range of skills and satisfaction the person is capable of developing
- **Esteem needs:** to enhance one's self-esteem
- **Acceptance needs:** to be loved and accepted by others
- **Safety needs:** to be both physically and psychologically safe and secure
- **Physiological needs:** to meet basic survival needs—food, drink, air, sex

Exercise 5.25

After all the assessment information has been collected together, the person who has overall responsibility for the assessment will be expected to organise, categorise, compare, and analyse all the information to produce a prioritised list of client needs/problems.

This information should be recorded in a way that makes it easy to plan the required services.

Planning Programmes of Care

You may be expected to take the lead in organising a care planning meeting. This includes the following:

- Disseminating relevant information to people who are going to attend the meeting (e.g., report from the needs assessment, supplementary information, time and venue)

- Booking a room and refreshments (e.g., tea and biscuits)

- Supporting the client and others to attend the meeting (e.g., arranging transport)

- Preparing the clients and others for the meeting (e.g., advising them of the care planning process and possible outcomes)

- Preparing a summary of the client's needs and wishes

The most important principle to follow in planning programmes of care is that there should be respect for client choice. A summary of the client's wishes and needs should be made available to everyone involved in the care planning meeting. Precise client need identification enables the individuals involved in planning care to prescribe specific action plans to meet specific needs. Specify preferred outcomes for each need or problem. Identify specific actions that are to take place in order to achieve the preferred outcomes. Then differentiate who is to provide the necessary services.

A "placement package" or "package of care" are terms used to describe the plans that have been agreed between the various agencies for meeting a client's needs. The package of care must meet personal care needs when clients are unable to do this for themselves. Clients need opportunities to participate in life-enhancing activities and occupations and the provision of opportunities to learn new skills that enable them to achieve greater independence.

Following is an example of a package of care:

- Warden who checks in on the client occasionally and who is also available in emergencies

- Neighbour who is willing to do the shopping

- Son who takes the client to his or her house for one day each weekend

- Home help three times a week

- Community nurse to change the dressings on the leg ulcers twice per week

- Voluntary agency who provides transport for the client to the twice-weekly club and escorts for hospital visits

As you can imagine, all these services take a lot of organising. This role is normally coordinated by a care manager, with a key worker being nominated as a first point of contact who will remain in touch with the client. Unfortunately, there can be problems when negotiating packages of care in terms of the following:

- The allocation and targeting of scarce resources

- The way that the different services are perceived by clients

- The knowledge and skills of everyone involved in the care planning process

Exercise 5.26 🖉

During the care planning meeting you should try to ensure the following:

- If the client is unable to comment on proposed services, someone should be appointed to speak on the client's behalf.

- Opportunities and time should be made available for everyone present at the meeting to listen and talk things through so that they can be empowered to participate fully in the decision making process.

- All options that are available to meet a client's identified needs are communicated to everyone at the meeting in ways which allow them to comment constructively on the options. The emphasis should be on creating realistic expectations for the client.

- When disagreements occur, the necessary time is taken to reach a workable resolution.

- The action plan proposed for the client is consistent with the client's agreed needs and any resource constraints.

The emphasis when putting these packages together should ensure that people and services mentioned are aware of the part they play in the provision of care and how they are supposed to integrate their services with all the others. There must be agreement between the client and those individuals providing the services. The plan should enable the client to have a better quality of life if goals are achieved.

In some care facilities, established policy may dictate the types of actions that can be undertaken and the individuals who will implement those actions.

Your contributions to the care-planning process can include the following:

- Ensuring that your contributions are clear, accurate, and made at the appropriate time

- Remembering that your behaviours and actions should represent the client's views,

not your employer's. You may need to support the client in putting his or her point of view across, especially when there are differences of opinion.

- Monitoring the client's and others' behaviour during the meeting (e.g., for medical reasons or if a client is likely to become aggressive). You may need to be careful how you describe the behaviours if you are not to put your own interpretations on them.

Exercise 5.27

The programme of care may involve the client and family in doing all or most of the actions themselves. Alternatively, a significant input from a number of professionals and care workers may be needed in a number of care environments to meet the client's needs. In some situations, it may be appropriate to include some off-the-shelf plans within the programme of care which can be adapted to meet individual client need. Off-the-shelf plans are appropriate when the situation calls for a specific set of actions or where the seriousness of the problem (when it happens) dictates that there will not be very much time for planning (e.g., a child has an asthma attack, an aggressive husband returns home drunk).

Exercise 5.28

Included in the programme should be a plan for periodic re-evaluation of progress in meeting the client's needs and problems. The client should be encouraged to contact the key worker if the situation changes and further assessment is necessary.

A well-written programme of care that is neat and concise provides a central source of information on the client and should be disseminated to an agreed list of people. It will outline the client's needs and the actions required to meet those needs. Following are the potential consequences of not clearly recording the decisions:

- There are likely to be omissions and mistakes in the delivery of care.

- Your employer might find it difficult to defend itself against client complaints.

- The document might be needed in a court of law or the coroner's court.
- It might be impossible to cost the package of care that is to be provided.

Once developed, the care programme or care package should not be regarded as a finished product. It is simply a guide to actions which can be altered or adapted to meet the changing needs of the client. Every effort should be made to utilise a method of storing the plan so that it is readily available to those who might need it and have the authority to access it. Where appropriate, the client should be able to seek help when difficulties are encountered. A helpline can be useful in these situations.

Reviewing Effectiveness

During implementation of the care plan, you should continue to collect data about the client's problems, needs, reactions, and feelings. This will allow an ongoing review of the effectiveness of the programme of care in meeting the client's needs.

An important aspect of review is to meet with the client and family in order to get feedback on the package of care being offered. In addition, when you are required to provide the client with physical care (e.g., bathing, feeding, changing a dressing), this can provide the opportunity for conversation and the chance to collect additional feedback, as long as you ensure the client does not feel vulnerable during this process.

The different agencies involved in the provision of care will also carry out some of their own assessments relating to their own responsibilities in the care package. It is important that these are available at any planned review meeting. A review meeting should be planned with the same meticulous attention to detail that would be expected for a care planning meeting.

Reviewing the effectiveness of care programmes is about evaluating the client's response to the programme of care including the effect that it is having on the client's quality of life. This is achieved by collecting data so that judgments can be made in terms of whether the goals of the programme of care are being achieved.

Exercise 5.29 🖉

Where appropriate, everyone who has been involved in the assessment, planning, and delivery of the programme of care should be involved in the review process. Discuss the effectiveness of the services in a way and at an appropriate level and pace that encourages everyone to take part. This includes a review of the following:

- Whether the goals of the care programme were appropriate and have been achieved, need to be changed, or need to be reprioritised

- Whether a previously identified problem is not really a problem

- The strengths and weaknesses of the various agencies who are providing services for the client

- Whether other agencies might more appropriately be providing aspects of care

- The effect of resource limitations on the services being offered to the client

- The ways that inter-organisational or multi-disciplinary working might contribute to more effective care

- The effect of the programme of care on the client's quality of life

- Any services that the client no longer wants

- Any other factors that might have affected the care programme

If any relevant party cannot be present at the meeting (e.g., the client), a summary of the views of the client should be available for everybody at the meeting. Everyone should be supported and encouraged to give opinions about the services, including ways that they might be improved.

Participants are encouraged to identify changes in the client's needs, social support systems, circumstances, and eligibility for services that may require alterations to service specifications and care plans. Recommendations for changing the plan of care should be discussed with all relevant parties. Discuss reasons why care services do not match the service specification and care plans and why the goals of care have not been met.

As with the planning process, records of the review process should be legibly and completely documented (e.g., signed, dated, and contain all relevant information) and communicated to everyone who needs to know.

Exercise 5.30 🖉

Summary

You are an important member of the care team—a group working together to achieve an identified result. An effective team depends on each of its members to contribute to the team's development and practice. Cooperation, trust, and respect for each other are vital to the team's success. Lifelong learning and personal development are important for staying up-to-date in your field; this includes reflecting on your experiences and learning from them. At the heart of care planning are the clients and their individual needs—physical, psychological, and societal. The care team has an important role in planning and reviewing care programmes to meet each client's needs.

Check Your Knowledge and Understanding

1. You used to get on really well with a colleague until you were promoted within the team. You were both considered for the promotion. Recently, she has been making a number of snide remarks in your presence, and you are getting feedback that she has started to take the mickey out of you behind your back. What should you do?

   a) Confront her in the corridor and say, "If you don't stop making snide remarks and taking the mickey behind my back, I'm going to make your life hell!"

   b) Ignore the problem in the hope that it will go away.

   c) Say to the person, "I have noticed a deterioration in our relationship since my promotion. I value your input into the team and our friendship. Can we have coffee together later and sort this out?"

   d) Ensure that you are as friendly as possible towards her, asking her opinions and including her in all the important decisions, in the hope that she will find it difficult to be horrible to you.

2. You gently feedback to a colleague that there have been a number of complaints about the quality of care that she has recently been providing. She does not accept responsibility and blames a shortage of resources and the rest of the care team for the problem. What would you do?

   a) Listen with an open mind, without interrupting, and try to discover why she is trying to lay the blame elsewhere. Then give her concrete examples where her care has not been up to standard, before moving on to looking at ways she might improve her performance, with her consent.

   b) Listen carefully to your colleague, but refuse to accept that the blame lies elsewhere. Insist that you plan together to overcome the problem.

   c) Accept what your colleague has said, and promise to give her another chance, whilst ensuring that you keep a closer eye on her future performance.

   d) Provide her with concrete examples of where her care has not been up to standard, before moving on to negotiating some corrective action that can be taken with her consent. Warn her that if her performance does not improve, she may face disciplinary action.

3. Your employing organisation announces that it is going to become a "learning organisation." It requests all employees to maintain a folder or portfolio (supplied by the employer) of learning experiences that occur at work. This includes details of formal study days attended and informal learning through reflecting on practice. Everybody is encouraged to attend the "Reflecting on Practice" workshop. In addition, the new performance appraisal system that is being implemented has incorporated the need for employees to show the "non-private" sections of their portfolios of learning experiences to the line manager. What would be your thoughts?

   a) "If they think they can force me to learn by going to a workshop and developing a portfolio, they can get stuffed! I've been doing this job for 15 years. There's not much they can tell me about this job."

   b) "OK, so I am expected to develop a portfolio. This doesn't sound like my 'cup of tea,' as I prefer formal classroom teaching

Module 5: Working Effectively Within Teams

and group work. But, I'll attend a workshop and have a go at reflecting on my practice. If I don't like it, I can always concentrate my personal development energies on the workshops."

c) "This sounds like an interesting opportunity. I'll go along to one of the workshops, pick up my portfolio, and have a go at reflecting on my practice. I am sure my friend Jo will be happy to give me some feedback on my work."

d) "This sounds like a good opportunity. I don't particularly like formal classroom teaching. I'll find myself a mentor and reflect on everything I possibly can to ensure that I have the biggest and best portfolio."

4. You are called in at short notice to a performance review by your very busy line manager. This is despite the fact that the policy states that you are supposed to be given a minimum of at least three weeks notice so that you can prepare for the appraisal by completing the prescribed form. He is obviously feeling stressed and uses the opportunity to criticise your work without giving any concrete examples of what you have been doing wrong. Eventually he provides you with your targets for the year. One or two of them appear to be impossible to achieve. What would you do?

a) Remind your manager that you have not had the chance to prepare for this appraisal, and you would like to think about the performance targets that he has set and see him the following week to discuss them.

b) Tell your manager that he is a bully and that you are going to report him to higher management for not following the performance appraisal policy.

c) Assertively and politely remind your manager that you have not had the chance to prepare for this appraisal and that you are not happy with his unsubstantiated criticisms and some of the targets that he would like to set for you. Request that you make another appointment for the appraisal in three weeks, at a time when he is not likely to be so busy.

d) Accept that your manager is an unorganised and stressed-out autocrat. Simply do your best with the targets that he has set for you.

5. A junior member of the care team has made a mistake at work which could have resulted in an accident. The mistake was due to her inexperience, rather than carelessness. What would you say to her?

a) "Let's look at how the mistake happened and see what we can learn from this incident."

b) "That was a really stupid mistake! I presume you will not be making that mistake again...or else!"

c) "You do realise that someone might have been killed? How would you have felt? Please make sure that you do not make this mistake again."

d) "I think you need to concentrate on completing your level 2 NVQ in Care. You wouldn't have made the mistake then."

6. Your employing organisation is having a new computer system installed which will store all client information. You will be expected to input client data on a fairly regular basis. Although you are a little frightened of computers, your employer is putting on a series of workshops so that staff can learn the necessary computer skills for their job roles. What would you do?

   a) Look around for employment opportunities where you can do the same or similar work without having to use computers.

   b) Negotiate with a computer loving colleague to do jobs for her if she is willing to input your data into the computer.

   c) Attend the workshop, and then do the best you can with inputting data to the new computer.

   d) Attend the workshop, and then ask a colleague to supervise you inputting data until you get the hang of it.

7. You have recently had a distressing experience when one of your clients with whom you had been working closely, committed suicide. You are feeling upset and feel sure that you should have seen this event coming and done something to prevent this from happening. What would you do?

   a) Reflect on the experience to see what can be learned from this critical incident.

   b) Talk to someone (e.g., colleague, counsellor, friend) about your feelings.

   c) Simply get on with the job because there are a lot of other people who require care.

   d) Apply to do a Suicide Awareness course at the earliest opportunity.

Module 6

Promoting Independence

Need-to-know words:

- bilirubin
- cardio-thoracic
- complementary health services
- eczema
- expectoration
- granulation tissue
- gynaecology
- haematology
- microbiology
- ophthalmic
- orthodontic
- orthoptic
- pathology
- podiatry
- psoriasis
- radiography
- urobilinogen

Enable others to look after themselves.

Objectives:

- Identify and describe the services and facilities that are available to others.
- Outline how to enable others to find out about and use available services and facilities.
- Discuss how clients can be helped to make decisions.
- Highlight how others can be helped to set personal budgets.
- Identify and describe the benefits and allowances that are available.
- Describe how others can be helped to claim and collect benefits and allowances.
- Describe how clients and their carers can be supported to undertake treatments and procedures.
- Describe the care needed by an individual who has an infection.
- Outline how to support individuals who are undertaking and interpreting specimen collection and physical measurements.

Module 6 Introduction

Module 6 relates to three units of the level 3 NVQ/SVQ Award in Care:

Unit Y2: **Enable others to find out about and use services and facilities** is an option group B unit. It consists of two elements of competence:

- Y2.1 Enable individuals to find out about services and facilities.

- Y2.2 Enable individuals to use services and facilities.

Unit Y3: **Enable individuals to administer their financial affairs** is an option group B unit. It consists of three elements of competence:

- Y3.1 Enable individuals to make payments.

- Y3.2 Enable individuals to claim benefits and allowances.

- Y3.3 Enable individuals to collect benefits and allowances.

Unit Y4: **Support individuals in undertaking health care** is an option group B unit. It consists of three elements of competence:

- Y4.1 Support individuals in undertaking procedures, treatments, and dressings.

- Y4.2 Support individuals in obtaining specimens and taking physical measurements.

- Y4.3 Support individuals to administer the client's own medication.

Part 1: Promoting Available Services and Facilities (Y2)

Enable people to access and use available services and facilities.

There is a wide range of individuals who may need help in finding out about, or accessing, available services and facilities:

- **Ordinary people** (e.g., clients and their families/dependants) who are simply not aware of available services and facilities

- **People in crisis** (e.g., due to bereavement, redundancy, homelessness, illness)

- Clients who are temporarily or permanently **mentally incapacitated** (e.g., due to mental illness, learning disability, drug toxicity, physical illness)

- Clients who have **communication difficulties** (e.g., due to the language used, inability to read or write, level of comprehension needed, deafness and blindness)

- People who have **financial or transport difficulties** who cannot access services

Exercise 6.1 🖉

Local care services undergo continuous change over the years for the following reasons:

- A changing local demand for services

- Changing national priorities for care

- The need to make efficiency savings

- Growing population, especially the elderly who need the most care services

- Changing family patterns (e.g., more one-parent families and unmarried mothers, fewer families who want to care for elderly relatives)

- Rising expectations of consumers

- New treatments being discovered

This has led to there being tremendous variations in the provision, availability, and quality of services and facilities in different parts of the country. You need to have an up-to-date knowledge of all relevant services and facilities that are available to your client group in your locality. If you do not know the relevant details, you will not be able to help others to find out about them.

People may need your support and help. Be flexible in your approach, if you are to be successful in enabling them to find out about and access services and facilities. The questions that individuals will usually ask about services and facilities include the following:

- What range of services and facilities are available?

- Where can I get further information about those services   addresses, telephone numbers?

- Am I likely to be charged for that service?

- Are there likely to be any restrictions on access to those services (e.g., lack of ramps, office opening and closing times, language barriers, public transport routes)?

- Can the service be provided without the client having to leave home?

Health Services

A wide range of health services are provided throughout the country. For a number of years, the range and quality of health services that must be provided by health authorities have been governed by the Patients Charter. This is due to be superseded by a set of national care standards and guidelines that will be produced by a National Institute of Clinical Excellence (Department of Health, 1997).

In the new organisation of health care within the United Kingdom, Primary Care Groups are being set up in each locality which will bring together general practitioners and community nurses in a given area. They have been given the responsibility for purchasing health services for their local communities, and they are expected to work closely with social services departments.

Hospital-Based Health Services

Although most hospital-based health care services are available in all health authorities, local variations occur. Some specialties of health care (e.g., cardio-thoracic surgery) are provided on a regional basis, rather than locally, because it is more cost-effective to do so. Some, usually smaller, health authorities purchase a few specialties from neighbouring districts because offering them locally is not cost effective.

Health care rationing is widespread throughout the National Health Service. Some health authorities have clear policies for rationing health services, whilst others do not. Waiting lists for specific care services vary both within and between health authorities.

Examples of hospital-based health services include the following:

- Specialty health care (e.g., gynaecology, maternity, surgery, ophthalmics, casualty, acute psychiatry)

- Ambulance service

- Pathology, haematology, and microbiology services

- Physiotherapy, occupational therapy, radiography
- Hospital pharmacy services
- Orthodontic and orthoptic services
- Out-patients
- Elderly rehabilitation services

Exercise 6.2 🖉

Community-Based Health Services

Following are examples of community-based health services:

- Dental services
- Opticians
- Podiatry/chiropody
- Community pharmacies
- School health services
- Health visiting services
- Community nursing services
- Learning disability services
- Health promotion services
- General practitioner services
- Drug rehabilitation services

Exercise 6.3 🖉

Information and advice on NHS services and standards, staying healthy, common illnesses, and waiting times can be obtained from the Health Information Service, telephone 0800 665544.

Local Authority Services

As part of community care, local authority care managers are expected to coordinate the assessment of client needs, negotiate packages of care to meet them, and monitor the effectiveness of the care delivered. Unfortunately, it has been found that community care services are sometimes not available or not flexible enough to meet client needs.

A Royal Commission on long-term care has been established. The Commission is expected to concentrate on ways of financing long-term care, although pressure groups are pushing for a resolution to the following issues:

- Why some care is provided free and other types of care have to be paid for
- The variations in price for different care services across the country
- The variations across the country in terms of the accessibility, availability, and quality of care

Following are examples of services available from local authorities:

- Domiciliary services (e.g., meals-on-wheels, tucking-in, home help, sitters-in, laundry service)
- Aids to living (e.g., ramps, widened doorways, bath and toilet adaptations)
- Residential services, day centres, and clubs (e.g., for people who are elderly or who have disabilities)
- Transport (e.g., to day centres)
- Social work services
- Fostering and adoption services
- Child protection services

Other Care Services

A range of care services is available from the voluntary and private sectors of the industry. The organisations who provide these services, although sometimes not well-financed, appear to have some advantages over public sector care agencies. They are better able to avoid bureaucratising the delivery of care (less red tape) and provide speed and flexibility in the provision of services for those who have an immediate need. Some specialise in minority groups (e.g., people who are HIV positive, unmarried mothers, the homeless, substance abusers).

Examples of available services are:

- Family shelters
- Special schools for people with specific problems (e.g., blind)
- Counselling services (e.g., the Samaritans)
- Housing associations
- Sheltered employment schemes
- Support schemes (e.g., Alcoholics Anonymous)
- Adoption and foster agencies
- Residential and nursing care homes
- Shelter for the homeless (e.g., from the Salvation Army)

Exercise 6.4 🖊

Local Services and Facilities

A range of other services will also be available locally:

- Housing services (e.g., sheltered accommodation, tenants exchange schemes, emergency accommodation)
- Education services (e.g., local authority schools, special schools for people with disabilities, FE colleges and universities, home visit teachers, youth services, means-tested free school meals and milk, subsidised transport to and from schools)
- Employment services (e.g., Job Centres, employment training, sheltered employment, "Back to Work" schemes, careers service, disabled resettlement officer)

- Legal services (e.g., legal representation, courts, prisons, and probation service)
- Spiritual services (available from a wide variety of churches and religious groups)
- Libraries
- Waste disposal services

There is a huge range of local facilities that will be available locally which clients may need more information about:

- Shops, centres, supermarkets	- Sports and health centres
- Churches/chapels/ synagogues/mosques	- Banks and building societies
- Post offices	- Bingo halls
- Solicitors	- Estate agents
- Cinemas	- Public houses

Exercise 6.5 🖊

Client Access to Relevant Information

To assess client needs for information, find a quiet place or room where you can talk confidentially. Follow these guidelines:

1. Use a counselling approach (see Module 2, Part 3).

2. Give the person time and space in which to express his or her needs.

3. Inform the client of rights pertaining to the situation (e.g., the right to a full assessment of needs as a basis for providing community care services to meet those needs).

4. Discuss available services at a level and pace that is appropriate to the person's ability to comprehend.

5. Check at intervals for the person's understanding of information and/or advice being provided. Provide additional information, if necessary.

6. Discuss access to other potential sources of information.

7. Outline potential sources of information, and ensure that those sources are appropriate for the client's personal beliefs and preferences.

Keep the following factors in mind when planning to meet a client's needs for information:

- The client should be encouraged to seek out and obtain his or her own information, where practical. If assistance is required, the amount and type of assistance should be negotiated (e.g., for advocacy, help with using the telephone, or writing a letter).

- The client should be encouraged to access services and facilities that are congruent with personal beliefs and preferences. For example, an individual should not be pressurised into putting an elderly relative into a residential home, if that person firmly believes that relatives should be cared for by the family.

- Any information that is provided to the client should be relevant, up-to-date, and in a format that can be understood. For example, a glossy brochure and leaflets are of little use to someone who is blind or cannot read very well.

- The client may need to be reminded that rights to confidentiality will be maintained in terms of the services that he or she chooses to access.

When the relevant information has been obtained by the client, there can be issues which may need to be managed. Where appropriate, ask the client to share with you the information that has been accessed and the source of that information.

You may need to point out any restrictions concerning the availability and targeting of services that the client would like to access. For example, it is difficult to get a tucking-in service that guarantees to get a relative in bed by a precise time.

Occasionally you will have to manage a client's reaction to discovering that a service is not available. This can involve getting past the initial disbelief and anger, and moving towards a search for alternative services or the provision of guidelines on how to cope without the service.

Sometimes a client will refuse a service, despite needing it (e.g., the stigma attached to receiving free school meals). You will have to decide whether to accept the person's right to refuse the service or attempt gentle persuasion to try and get the client to accept the service.

You may need to assess the likely effect on a client's overall care or a family carer's ability to cope, of the services that have been chosen by that client/carer. If unsure, seek advice.

Exercise 6.6

If you are not familiar with the types of services or facilities that are offered by any local care organisations, it might be worth visiting them to find out, at first hand, what they have to offer. Maintain an up-to-date folder that contains relevant information about the services that are available locally and likely to be needed by your client group.

Support others in using available services and facilities. Establish the type and level of assistance that is required to access the service or facility (e.g., escort, money, help to decipher timetables, make an appointment). Offer an appropriate level of support that enables the person to access the service or facility without leading to unnecessary dependence.

Either you or a friend can accompany the person, if appropriate, in the early days of accessing the service or facility until confidence is gained and independence has been achieved (e.g., accompanying a client to work, providing psychological support to overcome fears, assisting with communication difficulties). Enable the client to access services and facilities at a time which is likely to achieve the best outcomes.

Problems of access to services and facilities are discussed so that actions can be taken to reduce them (e.g., need for transport or an interpreter). You may need to make an ongoing check on whether the client is actually benefiting from access to a service/facility.

The aim of supporting others is to help them become as independent as possible. Therefore, be careful that you do not allow an individual or family to become unnecessarily dependent on you. Even when progress is very slow, always think to yourself, "What more could this person or family be doing for themselves in terms of accessing services and facilities."

Help Clients to Make Decisions. Three main factors involved in decision making are *authority*, *responsibility*, and *accountability*.

When helping a client to make a decision, it is important to be aware of your level of authority or power base. This is usually dependent on your care role and the place in which you are working.

Whenever possible, the responsibility for making a care decision should rest with the client and/or the family. At other times, the responsibility for making a care decision clearly lies with the care staff (e.g., deciding, after risk assessment, whether a client who has a learning disability should have free access to the kitchen to make a cup of tea when there is a risk of scalding him/herself).

The concept of choice for clients and the achievement of an acceptable quality of life is the goal of all care providers. Unfortunately, the shortage of resources within care agencies can result in clients and/or their families having little opportunity for involvement in the decision making process that is often referred to as needs-led assessment.

Therefore, in some situations, the client and/or family may not agree with a care decision that has been made by one of the parties. In this case, the basis on which the decision has been made needs to be clearly communicated to all relevant parties. It is essential that clear and factual information is used which takes account of factors such as differences in language and cultural expectations.

Exercise 6.7 🖉

Problems of Access

A recent report explored the provision of support services supplied to clients in their own homes—*floating support* (Douglas et al., 1998). The following problems were identified:

- Clients were often expected to make important decisions about their future care arrangements during times of crisis when they were least able to participate fully in the assessment and planning of their future.

- The current complexity of financial, legal, and institutional local arrangements for the provision of services resulted in clients usually having little choice and not being able to make informed choices about preferred care packages.

- Clients are not usually well-informed about the sources of funding for care services or their entitlements to care services. This limits their ability to exercise choice and control.

- When information is available to clients about availability of services, the information is not usually provided in a form that is easily understood.

- The majority of clients do not have the confidence or the "know how" to make a complaint.

Obtaining welfare benefits can be difficult. Following are some problems that clients may encounter:

- Lack of knowledge about available benefits
- Non-availability of application forms
- Complexity of rules and regulations
- Obscure language in leaflets
- Stigma involved in making a claim
- Poor customer services skills of officials

Admission to a care home has also been found to cause a number of problems (Wright, 1998). Many relatives find the process of choosing a care home from a given list to be intimidating because social workers usually decline to provide advice about individual care homes.

Many relatives are surprised that long-term care is means tested. That is, they can be charged for the care that is provided. The rules relating to the amount of savings a client is allowed to retain before those savings are used to pay for care, and the rules relating to a spouse's liability towards the costs of care, are open to local interpretation and, occasionally, flouted by local authorities. Very few relatives and friends are encouraged to be involved in the provision of care within the home.

Physical access problems to services and facilities may be illegal (due to the Disability Discrimination Act) and, therefore, the relevant organisation may need to be assertively challenged to improve access. For example, if the only access to council offices is up a flight of stairs, the council should be requested to provide a ramp or lift for wheelchair users and other people with mobility problems. If they refuse, or if there are unacceptable delays, more active ways of managing the situation may need to be taken. Following are examples:

- A letter of complaint to the local Council
- The completion of a formal Council complaints form
- A letter of complaint to the local MP or the local papers

There can also be risks attached to clients accessing services and facilities:

- To members of the public or people who are supporting the client (e.g., when a client is potentially aggressive or a potential abuser of others)
- To the client (e.g., in getting lost, being run over by a car, or being attacked and sexually abused)

All potential risks should be reviewed via a formal risk assessment which involves all relevant members of the multidisciplinary team, prior to the client accessing those services and facilities.

Client service evaluations should be undertaken on a regular basis by asking the following questions:

- Is the client/family coping?
- Is the client as healthy and safe as possible?
- Is the client/family satisfied with the type, timing, quantity, and quality of services they are receiving?
- Does the client/family experience an acceptable quality of life?

Exercise 6.8

Part 2: Helping Others to Manage Their Finances (Y3)

Enable others to look after their own financial affairs.

This section is concerned with supporting and enabling others to look after their own financial affairs so that they can become as independent as possible. It should be studied by those care support workers who are expected to provide help with clients' financial affairs as part of their work. The clients will normally have the responsibilities for managing the household budget.

The way an individual chooses to manage his or her finances depends on that person's values, attitudes, personal preferences, and previous experiences of seeing others manage (or mismanage) their finances. It is essential that you respect clients' wishes as to how they would like to manage their finances (even if that is not the way that you would prefer them to look after their money, or they have chosen a method that is not the best way to manage personal finances).

Exercise 6.9

You should agree the type and amount of support that the client requires. This is best achieved via a counselling approach. The client should be encouraged to be as independent as possible and can use informed choice in the management of his or her budget.

There should be an implicit agreement that you will disclose details of the client's finances only to those people agreed by the client. Having said that, if the client informs you that he or she chooses to do something that is illegal or against agency policies (e.g., make a false statement on a benefit claim form), you should make it clear that these endeavours cannot be supported.

Inform the client about the potential consequences of the actions. That is, he or she is likely to be caught and legal action taken, resulting in fines or imprisonment and loss of benefit. If the client knowingly goes ahead with illegal actions, let the client know that you will inform the appropriate authorities.

Personal Budgeting

When supporting a client to construct a personal budget, you are advised to assess the client's abilities to participate in the exercise. It is obvious that a client who has a severe learning disability or who is very confused most of the time, will not be able to actively participate, and a family member or advocate should be involved. For other clients, it may simply be a matter of getting them organised (e.g., ensuring there is a calculator, pen, and paper available) and checking the calculations.

The first thing that needs to be done is to identify sources of income. The sources of income that are identified should be those that are received on a regular basis, rather than one-off sources of income (e.g., a relative repaying a debt, a Community Care Grant). The various sources of income for each week or month should be listed and added up, including average wages of family members who are working and any benefits or allowances received by the client and/or other family members.

It is worthwhile at this time, to check the benefits and allowances that the client and the family receive against those that might potentially be claimed if the family knew they were eligible for them. The end result is that you should be able to calculate a figure for weekly/monthly income (e.g., £535 per month).

The second thing that needs to be done in preparing a budget is to identify and agree the client's regular payment obligations:

- Car loan
- Council Tax
- Gas
- Electricity
- Court fines
- Credit cards

139

- Insurance premiums
- Vehicle road tax
- Weekly shopping bill
- Rent/mortgage

Exercise 6.10 🖉

It may also be important to note when these payment obligations are due (e.g., monthly or yearly payment). The end result is that you should be able to calculate a figure for weekly/monthly outgoings (e.g., £480 per month).

Find out the client's preferences for ways of making payments. You may have to explain how the methods of payment differ. There are five main types of payment methods:

- Cheque: Certain types of bank and building society accounts provide a cheque book so that cheques can be written and sent off to make payments.

- Standing orders and direct debits: These are available with some bank and building society accounts. On completion of an appropriate form, they allow for a variable or an agreed sum of money to be automatically taken from the account each month.

- Giro and postal orders: A giro slip allows the payment to be made at any bank, building society, or post office by cash, cheque, or credit card. A postal order can be purchased from the post office and sent as a payment.

- Cash: This can be used flexibly, but is easily lost or stolen.

- Hire purchase and credit cards: These are methods of payment where a person can purchase items (e.g., carpets, car, washing machine, clothing) and pay for them over the following months or years. Although the client does not have to wait for the items that he or she wants, the rate of interest can be quite high when paying for goods in this way.

Disposable income is the difference between income and outgoing money. The client can choose what to do with disposable income (e.g., go to the pub, buy a pet, invest the money). Encourage the client to maintain a lifestyle that enables him or her (and the family) to live within the budget.

Exercise 6.11 🖉

Any problems and concerns relating to individual payments and the client's ability to pay should be discussed until a working solution can be found. If you are unsure or require help in this process, contact an appropriately qualified and experienced colleague.

A number of measures can be taken to help a client to more effectively manage his or her finances. These should be explained in a manner and at a level and pace that the client can understand. Finances can be a bone of contention within any family. This can result in the client becoming upset, especially if he or she is having difficulty being realistic in terms of income and lifestyle.

Your priority is to try and discover how acceptable the following measures are to the client:

- Look at the possibility of opening a bank or building society account. This provides more options for the client on how to meet payment obligations (e.g., cash, cheque, credit card, direct debit, standing order). Even clients who have a dreadful history and are financially blacklisted by credit companies can sometimes find a bank or building society that is willing to offer them a basic account.

- Explore the possibility of the client switching the bank account to one that does not have monthly account charges and that charges less interest for overdrafts.

- Assess the outgoings that are one-off payments, and see if they can be paid monthly so that payments can be spread over the whole year (e.g., Council Tax, gas, electricity).

- Explore the possibility of converting the majority of high interest credit/debit card debts into a single, low interest bank loan or overdraft.

- When outgoings are not covered by income, it may be necessary to assess where other savings can be made (e.g., moving to cheaper accommodations, getting rid of the car, buying clothes at car boot sales and charity shops, avoiding luxury foods).

- Look at the different ways that debts can be managed (e.g., deferred payments, splitting payments, asking a charitable organisation for support, agreeing to become bankrupt).

- When there is a large one-off payment to be made, look at the possibility of getting a loan from Social Security.

- Arrange for the client to get some professional advice on finances from an appropriate authority (e.g., Citizen's Advice Bureau).

Exercise 6.12 🖉

When helping or supporting a client to make payments, obtain receipts for bills and store these for future reference. Query any discrepancies in bills with the appropriate agency. Make sure that the client or a relative/advocate/guardian and your employing organisation are happy with you helping a client to manage his or her finances.

When making payments on behalf of a client, record details of money collected and payments made accu-

rately and legibly, according to your employing organisation's policies. All receipts should be saved to enable easy auditing of the client's account and so that faulty goods can be returned to the shop from which they were purchased. When the client queries the amounts of money that have been accessed and spent, the payments that have been made are clearly explained and accounted for.

Exercise 6.13 🖉

Claiming Benefits and Allowances

Full and comprehensive information on benefits and allowances can only be achieved by getting a copy of the relevant (and up-to-date) leaflets. Details are provided in the Suggested Reading section at the end of this book. Information on benefits and allowances is available from the Social Security Office, Citizen's Advice Bureau, and the Post Office.

In order to get precise details of the rules and regulations relating to benefits and allowances, clients should be strongly advised to visit the appropriate office (e.g., Social Security Office, Citizen's Advice Bureau, Council Housing Office) where they can pick up the latest leaflets and claims forms. The types of benefits and allowances that are available and the amounts of money that can be claimed can change significantly over the years.

Appointments can be made to talk to the relevant officers if an individual requires advice and further information relating to personal circumstances. Alternatively, a client can contact one of the enquiry lines listed at the end of this section.

Information is also available in a number of other languages. Ask for leaflet FB22 in the language of choice:

· Arabic	· Bangali	· Chinese	· Greek
· Gujarati	· Hindi	· Punjabi	· Turkish
· Urdu	· Welsh	· Vietnamese	

Exercise 6.14 🖉

The amount of benefit that is paid out to individuals and families is often dependent on a number of factors:

- Whether the individual has a partner
- The number of children living with the claimant, and their ages
- The family's earnings and other income
- The amount that is paid for child care so that the parent(s) can work
- Whether anyone in the family has a disability
- Whether special needs premiums are applicable

The following help can be provided to an individual who wants to claim or collect benefits or allowances:

- Agree the support that you can provide for clients whilst encouraging them to be as independent as possible. If necessary, participate in a risk analysis on the proposed care plan.
- Ensure that clients find out about the benefits and allowances that they are entitled to, even if you have to obtain the relevant information for them.
- Encourage clients to apply for all the benefits and allowances to which they are entitled, and respect their right to decide to not make a claim.
- Provide an appropriate amount of support so that all the relevant details are entered onto the claim form or benefit collection booklet, accurately and legibly.
- Support clients who may choose not to enter all the relevant information on a claims form, even when this results in reduced benefits, and as long as it does not result in individuals receiving more benefit than they are entitled to.
- Clients should be encouraged to check the amount of benefit or allowance received against the amount due. All discrepancies

should be reported to an appropriate authority.

Exercise 6.15 🖉

When helping a client to apply for and collect Social Security benefits, keep these issues in mind.

- Incomplete or illegible completion of a claim form can result in the client's claim being rejected or delayed. It can also result in a reduced amount of benefit being paid.
- Benefits can be provided more quickly if the claim form is taken directly to the Social Security Office, rather than by using the prepaid envelope supplied with the claim form.
- Most Social Security benefits are paid directly into a bank or building society account, or they can be collected as cash from a post office.
- Delays in making claims can result in lost benefits.
- Benefits and allowances need to be collected within a specified timescale, or they are likely to be withdrawn.
- The client should be informed that although confidentiality will be respected, if he or she deliberately misleads or misinforms when making a claim for a benefit or allowances, you will inform the relevant authority.
- The client's budget needs to take account of the method of payment (e.g., cheque, claim book) and the timescales of payment (e.g., monthly).
- The client should be encouraged to take steps to ensure that all monies received are kept in a safe and secure place. This can range from using a "bum bag" when collecting monies, to having the monies paid directly into a bank or building society, rather than keeping it under the mattress.
- Some arrangement may need to be made so that a client who does not have a bank account can cash cheques.

142

- Some care settings may require an accurate record to be kept of a client's funds so that they are available for inspection by auditors. If the client refuses to keep cash and valuables in a safe and secure place, he or she may be required to sign a disclaimer form.

- Any loss of cash or valuables should be reported to an appropriate authority (e.g., the police, the person-in-charge, a senior officer), without delay.

You may need to inform or remind a client receiving welfare benefits as a result of an accident, injury, or disease, that if he or she is successful in making a claim for compensation, the eventual compensation award may be reduced to take account of any benefits paid for the same purpose.

Exercise 6.16

Remember that Social Security benefits are usually paid to help a client cope with everyday life, illness, and disability in the home. Therefore, if a client or dependant member of the family goes into hospital, some of these needs will be met by the NHS. This can result in the welfare benefit being reduced or stopped. The Social Security Office should be informed as soon as a member of the family enters hospital, and when the person is discharged so that the welfare benefits can resume being paid in the usual way.

Examples of Benefits and Allowances

Attendance Allowance is a tax-free welfare benefit that is not dependent on National Insurance contributions. It is available to individuals ages 65 years or over who need help with personal care because of an illness or disability. It is not affected by level of income or savings, and it is usually ignored as income in terms of Jobseeker's Allowance claims. To get Attendance Allowance, the person will usually have needed help with personal care for at least six months. Special rules govern terminal illness so that benefit can be awarded more quickly.

Back to Work Benefits consist of two main types—Back to Work Bonus and Child Maintenance Bonus. The Back to Work Bonus can provide a tax-free lump sum on return to work if the individual has been out of work for at least three months, or has worked part-time and earned more than a certain amount per week whilst receiving Jobseeker's Allowance and/or Income Support.

The Child Maintenance Bonus is available to an individual who receives child support maintenance, but leaves Income Support or income-based Jobseeker's Allowance because that person or the person's partner has started work, increased working hours, or increased earnings.

Child Benefit is a tax-free weekly payment for nearly all people, regardless of National Insurance contributions, who have responsibility for a child. The benefit is usually paid on four-weekly basis. It is available for each child under 16 years of age and for those between 16-19 years of age if they are still in full-time education. Child Benefit is paid until the end of the summer holidays of the year in which the child has left full-time education.

Soon after a baby is born, the parent(s) will receive a pack entitled "Claiming Child Benefit." Usually, it is expected that the child's mother will claim the benefit. For unmarried couples where only one is the child's parent, it is expected that the parent will make the claim. A higher rate of Child Benefit may be available to single parents.

The Guardian's Allowance can be claimed in addition to Child Benefit by an individual who takes care of a child who has lost both parents. Occasionally, the allowance can be paid where just one parent is dead and the parents were divorced or never married, or where the surviving parent is in prison or cannot be traced.

Exercise 6.17 ✎

Child Support Maintenance is organised by the Child Support Agency. Any individual who is living with, and caring for, a child can apply to have Child Support Maintenance assessed and collected by the agency from an absent parent. If an individual and/or the person's partner are receiving Income Support, income-based Jobseeker's Allowance, Family Credit, or Disability Working Allowance, the agency may require that individual to seek Child Support Maintenance.

An individual who receives Child Support Maintenance, but lost Income Support or income-based Jobseeker's Allowance because that individual or partner starts work, increases working hours, or increases earnings, may also qualify for a Child Maintenance Bonus.

Criminal Injuries Compensation can be claimed if an individual is physically or mentally injured as a result of a crime of violence. The injury must be serious enough to qualify for the minimum award to £1,000. An individual can also qualify for the award if he or she is a dependant or relative of a victim of a crime of violence who has since died. The amount of the award is dependent on the severity of the injuries sustained.

Disability Living Allowance is a tax-free benefit that is not affected by National Insurance contributions, by savings, or level of family income. It is usually ignored as income for Income Support and Jobseeker's Allowance claims. This allowance is available to individuals who have a child who needs help with personal care or with mobility, or both. This care must have been needed for the previous three months and is likely to be needed for a further six months.

There are two components to Disability Living Allowance:

- The *care component* is for children who need a lot of help with personal care. There are three rates. The highest rate is paid for the child who needs help both day and night. The middle rate is paid when help is needed for the child, either during the day or during the night. The lower rate is paid if the child needs help during the day.

- The *mobility component* is for children aged five years and over who need help with mobility. The higher rate is paid for a child who is (virtually) unable to walk because of a physical disability, or if the child had both legs amputated at or above the ankle, or if the child was born without legs or feet, or if the child is both deaf and blind, or if the child has a severe learning disability and exhibits challenging behaviour and qualifies for the higher rate of the care support. The lower rate is paid to provide guidance and supervision for a child when outdoors in unfamiliar areas.

To receive the higher rates of both the care and mobility components, the child under 16 years of age must need substantially more attention than a "normal" child of the same age. Special rules apply to a child who has a terminal illness who is not expected to live for more than six months. The care component can be paid right away, even when they do not need care at the time when the Disability Living Allowance commences.

Exercise 6.18 ✎

Disability Working Allowance is a tax-free, income-related benefit for individuals who have illnesses or disabilities that limit their ability to earn a wage.

- The individual must be at least 16 years old.

- The individual must be working an average of at least 16 hours per week (more benefit is available if working over 30 hours per week).

- The individual must be receiving another benefit (e.g., Disability Living Allowance, or Attendance Allowance, or War Disablement Pension with War Pensioner's Constant Attendance Allowance/Mobility Supplement, or Industrial Injuries Disablement Benefit with Constant Attendance Allowance).

- This allowance is not given if the individual is on a training scheme and receiving an allowance.

- The individual must pass a disability test (declare that he or she suffers from one of the circumstances that qualify as a disability that limits work opportunities).

Once awarded, Disability Working Allowance is paid at the same rate for 26 weeks, even if earnings and other circumstances change during that period.

Family Credit is a tax-free cash benefit for low-income working families who have children. At least one parent must be working an average of at least 16 hours per week. The parent must have responsibility for at least one child under the age of 16 years (or under 19 years if in full-time education). Family credit is not given if the family has savings of £8,000 or more. Savings between £3,000 and £8,000 will reduce the amount of benefit that is given.

Individuals who claim Family Credit are given a statement of how much they can earn and still claim the benefit. Once awarded, Family Credit is paid at the same rate for 26 weeks, even if earnings and other circumstances change during that period.

Exercise 6.19 🖉

Free and Reduced-Price Milk and Vitamins can be made available to families receiving Income Support or income-based Jobseeker's Allowance. A pregnant woman and children under five years of age receive free milk and vitamins.

In addition, a family who is receiving Family Credit and has a child under the age of one year who is not being breast-fed, is allowed to purchase reduced-price, dried baby milk from a Maternity Clinic or Child Health Clinic.

Help with Health Costs is available if an individual belongs to one of the category groups specified (e.g., individuals already receiving Income Support, income-based Jobseeker's Allowance, Family Credit or Disability Working Allowance, individuals with specific medical conditions, individuals who are housebound or live in a care home). The individual and partner receive the following free:

- NHS prescriptions
- NHS dental treatment
- NHS sight tests
- NHS wigs and fabric supports

They also receive vouchers towards the cost of glasses or contact lenses. Refunds are available for necessary travel costs to and from hospital for NHS treatment for the family, the partner, and dependants under 19 years of age.

Housing/Council Tax Benefit are Social Security benefits offered by local councils to individuals who need help to pay their rent, housing costs, and Council Tax. It cannot be used for mortgage interest payments, some service charges, fuel, or food. An individual's rights to Housing or Council Tax Benefit are not dependent on National Insurance contributions.

Housing/Council Tax Benefit is provided when the amount of money coming into a household is lower than that allowed for the family's need, after taking into account any other benefits that the family may receive.

The benefit is not given if the family has savings of £16,000 or more. Savings between £3,000 and £16,000 will reduce the amount of benefit that is given. Some individuals who are living in a care home are allowed to keep £10,000 in savings before the benefits are reduced or stopped.

Exercise 6.20 🖉

There are three potential components to Housing Benefit:

- A *personal allowance* for the individual making the application (and the applicant's partner)
- A *dependant's allowance* if the individual has dependent children or young people living with him or her
- *Premiums* for special needs (e.g., for individuals who are elderly or disabled and for those looking after children)

Council Tax Benefit can also include a Second Adult Rebate if a person of at least 18 years is living in the household who is not the applicant's partner, on a low income, and not paying rent.

The maximum Council Tax Benefit is 100 percent of a family's Council Tax liability. However, families living in houses that are band F, G, and H properties will only receive the maximum Council Tax Benefit applicable to band E properties.

Home Responsibilities Protection is a special arrangement that has been made available to protect a person's Retirement Pension and a wife's right to Widow's Benefit. It works by reducing the number of years National Insurance contribution are needed to qualify for a basic pension. Married women who have retained their right to pay a reduced rate of National Insurance contributions are not eligible for Home Responsibilities Protection. It is available to individuals who look after a child or a sick or disabled person who does not work at all, or works, but does not pay enough National Insurance contributions in a tax year for it to count for Retirement Pension purposes.

Exercise 6.21 🖉

Incapacity Benefit is for individuals under state pension age who are unable to work because of illness or disability and who have paid enough National Insurance contributions during their lifetime.

Short-term Incapacity Benefit is the highest rate of benefit and is paid to individuals who are still sick after a year. It is also paid to individuals who are entitled to the highest rate care component of Disability Living Allowance and to individuals who are terminally ill.

Incapacity benefit cannot be claimed if the individual was over the state pension age when the illness began. If the illness began before state pension age, short-term Incapacity Benefit may be paid at the retirement pension rate for up to a year of incapacity.

Extra money can be added to the Incapacity Benefit if the claimant's husband or wife is aged 60 years or more, if an adult has to care for the children, or the claimant has children.

The decision as to whether a person is incapable of work is taken by an adjunction officer. For the first 28 weeks of sickness, an individual's ability to do the job is assessed by the individual's general practitioner. After that time, the individual has to be more formally assessed in terms of the ability to carry out a range of work-related activities and will usually include an examination (work test) by a specially appointed doctor.

An individual is allowed to undertake voluntary or therapeutic work whilst receiving Invalidity Benefit, as long as the work is less than an average 16 hours per week. The therapeutic work must be viewed as having a positive effect on the individual's condition, and the individual must not earn more than £48 per week after deduction of allowable expenses.

Exercise 6.22 🖉

Income Support is a Social Security benefit for individuals of 16 years or over whose income is below a set level. It can be paid in addition to other earnings from part-time work and benefits. The right to Income Support does not depend on National Insurance contributions.

- The individual must normally be resident in the United Kingdom.
- The individual must not be working in excess of an average of 16 hours per week, or the individual's partner (if there is one) must not work in excess of an average of 24 hours per week.
- The individual is not expected to sign on as unemployed and must meet one or more of the following criteria:
  - Incapable of employment due to sickness or disability
  - Raising children on his/her own
  - Aged 60 years or over
  - Caring for someone who has a disability
  - Registered blind
- Income support is not given if the family has savings of £8,000 or more. Savings between £3,000 and £8,000 will reduce the amount of benefit that is given.
- If the individual is resident in a care home, benefit will not be provided if the person has savings of £16,000 or more. Savings between £10,000 and £16,000 will affect the amount of benefit that is paid.
- Income support can be provided to help pay housing/mortgage costs or to help an individual pay for his/her residential care costs.
- Individuals who are still at school and over 16 years can claim Income Support if the individual meets the following criteria.
  - Is looking after his/her own child
  - Is an orphan and no one is caring for him or her
  - Is so disabled that he or she is unlikely to get a job
  - Is separated and not in touch with parents or anyone acting in their place, or separated from parents for reasons that cannot be avoided (e.g., they are in jail)

Income Tax allowances are available for single-parent families. An individual raising a child alone should be able to claim additional personal allowances on top of the single person's allowance. These allowances add up to the same as the married allowance. Advice should be sought from the local Income Tax Office.

Exercise 6.23

Industrial Injuries Disablement Benefit is available to employees who become disabled because of an accident at work or due to one of the prescribed diseases. It is tax free and can be paid in addition to Incapacity Benefit. The amount that the individual is paid depends on the level of disability. A 14 percent disablement is the lowest rate of benefit (except for certain respiratory diseases), and the max-imum is paid for 100 percent disablement. Other allowances are also available:

- *Reduced Earnings Allowance* is paid for an individual who cannot return to his or her usual work or do work of the same standard because of the disability. This allowance will not continue when a woman reaches 60 years and a man reaches 65 years. It is usually replaced by a Retirement Allowance.

- *Constant Attendance Allowance* is available when the disability has been assessed as 95 percent or more and that individual needs constant care and attention. There are four rates which depend on the amount of attention required.

- *Exceptionally Severe Disablement Allowance* is available to those who are receiving Constant Attendance Allowance at the higher levels when the care and attention needed is likely to be permanent.

Additional tax-free benefits are available to individual's and their dependants when that individual suffers from one of the specified diseases such as pneumoconiosis.

Invalid Care Allowance can be claimed by individuals of working age, if they are caring for a severely disabled person who receives the Disability Living Allowance at the middle or higher rate, Constant Attendance Allowance, or Attendance Allowance. The claimant must be caring for the person for at least 35 hours per week and not earn more than £50 per week after deductions for allowable expenses.

Jobseeker's Allowance is a Social Security benefit available for individuals who are unemployed. The individual must meet the following criteria:

- Be actively seeking work

- Be capable and available for work

- Normally be between 18 years and pension age

- Have an agreed Jobseeker's Agreement which outlines what the individual intends to do to find work

If the individual has paid enough National Insurance contributions, the person will receive a calculated rate of contribution-based Jobseeker's Allowance for up to 182 days. If the individual has not paid enough National Insurance contributions to qualify, or if the contribution-based rate is not enough to meet the person's needs, the person may qualify for income-based Jobseeker's Allowance.

Exercise 6.24

Severe Disablement Allowance can be claimed by people who have a disabled child, aged 16 years or more, who has been incapable of work for at least 28 weeks. A young person aged between 16 and 19 years who is incapable of work, but is receiving education, may be able to get Severe Disablement Allowance if the programme of study is less than 21 hours per week.

The **Social Fund** helps individuals who have expenses that are difficult to pay out of that person's usual income. An individual can get help from the Social Fund if the person is already receiving Income Support or the income-based Jobseeker's Allowance, irrespective of National Insurance contributions. Payments are provided for the following family/household costs:

- Cold Weather Payment and Winter Fuel Payments: to help pay the heating bills during very cold weather

- Maternity Payment: to help buy the essentials for a new baby

- Funeral Payments: to help pay funeral costs

- Community Care Grant: to help people who have special needs with certain travel and living costs

- Budgeting Loans: to meet an important one-off expense (e.g., to get the house rewired)

- Crisis Loan: to meet an individual's immediate needs in an emergency or following a disaster where otherwise, there might be a serious risk to a family's health or safety

Local **Social Services** departments can provide help for a disabled individual to access a number of services and facilities:

- Local bus and train fares

- Day nurseries and playgroups

- Special equipment and home adaptations

- Holidays

- Home care assistants
- Residential accommodation
- Day centres
- Meals-on-Wheels
- Special housing
- Laundry service
- Telephone provision

Exercise 6.25

Statutory Maternity Pay is available to female employees who are expecting babies, even if they do not intend to return to work. Following is eligibility criteria for the employee:

- Has been in the same employment without a break for at least 26 weeks including the 15th week before the week the baby is due (referred to as the qualifying week)

- Has average earnings at or above the lower earnings limit (where National Insurance contributions have to be paid)

Statutory Maternity Pay is paid up to 18 weeks. The earliest it can start is 11 weeks before the baby is due. However, it can be delayed until the baby's birth without losing benefit. Following are rules that are linked to Statutory Maternity Pay:

- The individual has to inform the employer that she intends to stop work because of pregnancy (at least three weeks before the date she intends to stop work).

- A maternity certificate form has to be given to the employer (provided by a doctor or midwife).

- Statutory Maternity Pay can be paid out even if the individual is working outside the United Kingdom.

Those individuals who do not quality for Statutory Maternity Pay (e.g., self-employed or have recently changed jobs) may be able to get the Maternity Allowance if they have paid enough National Insurance contributions. When an individual is already off work and receiving Statutory Sick Pay, this will stop when the person receives Statutory Maternity Pay or the Maternity Allowance. If an individual is not eligible for Statutory Maternity Pay or the Maternity Allowance, she may be able to get Incapacity Benefit. If she has been working recently. The maternity certificate is accepted as evidence of incapacity to work for the period starting six weeks before the baby is due.

Exercise 6.26

Statutory Sick Pay can be claimed by an individual who is employed and earns more than the minimum earnings limit for payment of Class I National Insurance contributions. It is available when a person is off sick for four or more days in a row (including weekends and Bank Holidays). It is paid by the employer for up to 28 weeks. Periods of illness with less than eight weeks between them count as one spell. Income tax and National Insurance contributions are deducted from Statutory Sick Pay.

A **War Pension** is available to individuals who have served in the Armed Forces during wartime and were injured or disabled. A War Pension is also available to other individuals who were injured or disabled during war (e.g., Civilian Defence Volunteers, prisoners of war). War pensioners can receive help with health costs and, together with War Widows, can also receive a Christmas Bonus. Help is also available to pay the costs of a war pensioner's funeral.

Widow's Payment is available to an individual when her husband has died. At present, this is a tax-free payment of £1,000. The widow must be under state pension age, or her deceased husband must not have been entitled to a Retirement Pension when he died.

In addition, a widow may be able to get the Widowed Mother's Allowance. This is a taxable weekly benefit for widows of any age who have at least one child for whom they receive Child Benefit. It is also available if the widow is expecting a child by the deceased husband or as a result of artificial insemination or in vitro fertilisation. If the husband died before 11th April 1988, the allowance can be made available even if the woman is not receiving Child Allowance, as long as there is a child under 19 years of age living in the household.

The individual receives a basic rate plus an addition for every child which received Child Benefit. This is in addition to the earnings-related pension that the husband had earned in his lifetime.

Exercise 6.27 ✐

Enquiry Lines

Additional information on specific benefits and allowances can be obtained from the following confidential enquiry lines:

• Benefit Enquiry Line	0800 882200
For people with speech or hearing problems who have access to a text-phone	0800 243355
• Child Support Agency National Enquiry Line	0345 133133
• Criminal Injuries Compensation Authority	0141 3312726
• Disability Discrimination Act Information Line	0345 622644
• Family Credit Helpline	01253 500050
• Health Information Service	0800 665544
• War Pensions Helpline	01253 858858

Part 3: Supporting Others to Undertake Health Care (Y4)

Enable people to meet their own health care needs.

This module is primarily concerned with preparing and supporting clients, or carers on behalf of the clients, to undertake health care activities. The assumption is that the client is living in the community or in a rehabilitation facility and is being prepared for discharge. There are a number of reasons why a client or a carer should be encouraged to undertake health care activities. Following are examples:

• Many health care activities are relatively simple. They do not need to be carried out by a qualified health care professional.

• This releases limited health care resources for the clients who really need them.

• It can result in a client being discharged from a health care facility much earlier than normal.

• The need for continuing care can be quite depressing. The ability to be independent in the provision of health care can be a real morale booster. It allows the client and carer to fit the health care activities within the "normal" flow of the day, rather than be dependent on others.

The care worker's role is to provide the necessary support and encouragement so that the health care activities are completed according to the agreed plan of care. The aim is that the client receives a quality of care that is as good as that provided by qualified and experienced health care workers.

Exercise 6.28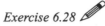

Using a counselling approach, establish that the person is willing and able to undertake the health care activity. Encourage the client or carer to be as independent as possible (although you may need to accept that total independence in undertaking the health care activity may never be achieved).

Explore any fears that the individual may have in taking responsibility for the health care activity (e.g., the fear of making a mistake, what to do when there is a problem, who to call for help).

Explain that the person will not be expected to undertake the health care activity until the following criteria are met:

- Both of you are sure that the person has developed the necessary competence.

- The necessary materials and equipment are readily available.

- Agreement has been reached on the level and type of support, assistance, and supervision that is provided to enable the health care activity to be undertaken safely.

- You are confident that part of the health care activity can safely be devolved to the client/carer.

When health care activities have to be undertaken in the home situation, the usual guidelines or treatment regime used in a formal health care setting may need to be adapted so that the client and carer can return to as "normal" a lifestyle as possible. This may lead to the care plan having to be changed. The following arrangements will minimise inconvenience.

- Health care activities should be integrated within the normal flow of the client's/carer's daily routine, as long as this does not reduce the effectiveness of the treatment regime.

- Arrangements for the procurement and safe storage of materials and equipment will need to be arranged (e.g., setting aside a cupboard within the house for the medical equipment, dressings, and lotions). In the event of shortages, the individual will need to know how to access the emergency supplies or cope without the usual materials and equipment.

- Arrangements for the safe disposal of infected or contaminated waste will need to be made with the local authority and health authority (e.g., the provision of coloured plastic bags and a collection service).

Do not be afraid to involve other members of the care team in this process, especially when you are asked questions that you cannot answer.

Exercise 6.29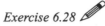

When working with a client or carer to develop competence in undertaking a health care activity, you may find it useful to follow this process:

1. Make two lists. One list is what the individual needs to know about the heath care activity (e.g., basic anatomy and physiology, how to recognise adverse reactions and problems, the reasons why hand cleansing and the appropriate disposal of clinical waste are important). The second list is what the individual should be able to do in order to undertake the activity safely (e.g., how to undertake an aseptic technique, how to change a colostomy bag).

2. Assess the person's current knowledge, capabilities, and confidence concerning the health care activity. This will then allow you to determine the areas of the health care activity on which the client/carer needs to concentrate.

3. Negotiate a plan to enable the client/carer to achieve the necessary competence in the health care activity. Depending on the

individual's previous knowledge and abilities, the normal sequence of events follows this pattern:

- The individual observes the health care activity being carried out.

- The health care activity is practised under supervision until competence is demonstrated.

- The client/carer commences independent practice of the health care activity (with an agreed level of support or supervision, if required).

Exercise 6.30 🖉

Supporting Independence

Guidelines relating to specific health care activities and procedures are provided in other parts of this study guide. The information available in this guide can be used as a basis for teaching the correct technique and relevant theory relating to a treatment or aspect of care that a client or carer would like to undertake independently. You should also search for more comprehensive teaching resources available locally (e.g., leaflets, booklets, teaching packs). If unsure, ask an appropriate member of the care team for advice.

When a treatment or procedure is being carried out by a client or carer, the level of supervision provided should ensure the following:

- The immediate area is appropriately prepared for the treatment or procedure to be undertaken (e.g., windows closed, curtains or screens drawn, the necessary equipment and materials are available and to hand).

- Appropriate cross-infection precautions are taken (e.g., hand washing before and after the treatment, correct aseptic technique, appropriate disposal of clinical waste).

- The individual undertaking the activity uses the correct technique at an appropriate place and time, according to the plan of care.

- The client or carer is given appropriate feedback on his or her performance. The emphasis should be on praising the individual who does well and providing guidance when a mistake is made. Try not to be over-critical and do not be afraid to step in if the client/carer is struggling or appears to be about to do something dangerous (e.g., use a dressing that has been contaminated by being dropped on to the floor).

Following are examples of procedures, treatments, and dressings that a client or carer may want to take on:

- **Dressings** (e.g., to wounds, pressure sores, leg ulcers)

- **Care of lesions** (e.g., skin treatments for psoriasis or eczema)

- **Elimination** (e.g., catheter care, changing urine drainage bags, prevention and management of constipation, stoma care, continence management)

- **Pressure area** care

- **Manual handling** (the carer learning how to move a client or the client learning how to move independently)

- Managing **challenging behaviour**

- **Infection control** (e.g., if a family member is HIV positive)

- Management of **epileptic seizures**

- **Tube feeding** for clients who cannot eat or drink orally

- **Personal hygiene** (e.g., bed baths, use of special bathing equipment)

Exercise 6.31 🖉

The person undertaking the health care activity needs to be aware of any changes in the client's condition. Changes may occur due to natural deterioration in the client's condition or because there is progress in, or reaction to, the treatment. Where appropriate, the client or carer should be encouraged to do the following:

- Collect and test specimens of body fluids (e.g., test the urine and blood of people who have diabetes)

- Undertake physical measurement (e.g., test the vital capacity in chronic lung disease, check the blood pressure in chronic kidney disease)

- Maintain vigilance by using observational skills and interpreting test results in order to identify and report any significant changes in the client's condition.

- Ask whether the client is feeling comfortable or if he or she feels there is a problem (e.g., feeling very uncomfortable due to having to lie in the same position for more than 10 minutes whilst a clinical activity is completed).

When there are adverse changes in the client's condition, it may be necessary for the carer to cease the clinical activity. The carer must then seek advice from an appropriate member of the care team without delay.

The changes in a client's condition are dependent on the basic illness or disability from which the client is suffering, and the treatments or procedures that are being undertaken on the client. One change in a client's condition, that is quite common, is an infection.

Preventing Infections

The carers of clients who are at risk from an infection should be provided with relevant information about preventing infections. Although the principles of infection control are provided in Module 3, Part 2, additional information is provided here.

Environmental Control can be used to prevent infection. Examples of environmental issues include *cleaning dust* and *waste disposal*.

Cleaning dust is a reservoir of micro-organisms. Therefore, cleaning should concentrate on its removal (rather than its redistribution). Floor cleaning should be carried out by vacuums fitted with filters, rather than dusters. Mops are a potential breeding ground for bacteria, especially those used to mop up bodily fluids. They should be thoroughly washed in water, then soaked in a solution of Sudol 1 percent and then rinsed and dried.

Waste disposal is an important issue. Some of the materials used for procedures, treatments, and dressings are hazardous because they are an infection risk to others. Unless properly organised, their disposal can cause a problem as there is a duty of care under the Environmental Protection Act (1990). Arrangements can usually be made with the local health authority for their collection and disposal by incineration.

Sharps (e.g., syringes and needles, glass ampoules, scalpel blades) should be carefully placed in a rigid sharps box. Other non-sharp, disposable materials (e.g., used dressings and bandages, catheters) that are contaminated by body fluids, need to be placed in a waterproof (usually yellow) sack so that they can also be collected and incinerated by the local health authority.

Exemptions to the duty of care under the Environmental Protection Act are available to homeowners who produce relatively small amounts of clinical (controlled) waste. Here, soiled items such as incontinence aids and nappies can be wrapped in newspaper, where appropriate, and double bagged prior to being disposed of in the household rubbish.

Exercise 6.32 🖉

In order for bacteria to thrive, they need a favourable environment (like the human body), temperature of around 37°, moisture, food supply, and slight alkalinity. Some require a supply of oxygen, whilst others require oxygen to be absent.

In response to invasion by bacteria and damage to any part of the body, local inflammation is the body's natural response. First, there is a dilation of the blood vessels in the affected area. The local blood vessel walls leak fluid into the area to dilute any toxins that have been released by the bacteria and create a physical barrier to further spread of the infection. The leaked fluid also contains blood cells that can kill bacteria and get rid of any dead tissue. The inflammation causes swelling and pressure on the nerve endings, resulting in pain.

Other typical signs and symptoms of an infection include the following:

- A raised body temperature which may result in sweating and shivering

- An increase in pulse and respiration rate

- Swelling, redness and warmth (inflamed) at the site of infection (if on the surface)

- More pain than would be expected from the original illness or wound

Other factors can affect the body's ability to fight infection, including age, hormones, and health of the person.

- Age: The very young and the very old are at greater risk from infection than other age groups.

- Hormones: Clients receiving steroid therapy are much more likely to get an infection.

- Health: Individuals who are debilitated through illness or who are malnourished are less able to fight an infection.

Exercise 6.33 🖉

When a client appears to have an infection, the client or carer should be encouraged to contact the doctor so that antibiotics can be prescribed. The three most common sites for infection are wounds (the skin), the respiratory tract, and the urinary tract.

To prevent **wound infection**, follow these guidelines:

- Carers with infected skin lesions and sore throats should avoid changing wound dressings.

- Sterile packs should be checked for damage and expiry dates.

- All equipment needed for dressings should be collected in advance because interruptions in the smooth flow of the procedure expose the wound unnecessarily.

- The hands must be thoroughly washed at the beginning of the procedure.

- The correct method for opening a sterile pack should be used so that the contents are not contaminated.

- Soiled dressings should be removed carefully to prevent scattering bacteria into the air, and discarded into a plastic bag for later incineration.

- Neither a wound nor any sterile material should be touched by hand.

- Infections are minimised by avoiding unnecessary talking, avoiding unnecessary movement, minimum exposure of wounds, and minimum disturbance of clothing and linen.

Once the natural barrier of the skin has been breached, a wound is a good home for bacteria. The infection can originate from the client's own natural body micro-organisms or from a number of other sources such as bedding, dust, infections carried by carers (e.g., colds, boils, unwashed hands).

Wound infections are characterised by an increased wetness to the wound (even if pus has not yet started to develop), and an increase in pain from the wound. There will be a change in the appearance of the granulation tissue which will appear to be very fragile, wet, and a deeper red than normal.

Exercise 6.34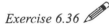

Chest Infections are characterised by a rattling cough, the production of copious amounts of yellow/green sputum, and difficulty with breathing.

Some chest infections are preventable by the provision of high quality care. Clients may have restricted breathing because of illness or post-operative pain. The inadequate lung ventilation leads to a retention of secretions in the respiratory passages which create an excellent breeding ground for bacteria. To help prevent a chest infection, consideration should be given to the following:

- Maintaining an appropriate position for the client to be able to breathe easily

- Ensuring that there are frequent changes of position

- Providing chest physiotherapy that encourages the client to expectorate lung secretions

- Using suction to keep the respiratory passages clear, if necessary

The collection of sputum requires special consideration. Disposable cartons with lids should be used, and they should be changed frequently. Paper tissues should be used in the place of handkerchiefs, and the carer's hands should be thoroughly washed after handling sputum cartons or used tissues.

Exercise 6.35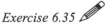

In most cases, **urinary infections** are due to bacteria on the outside gaining access to the bladder via the urethra. Most infections are due to the bacteria which live in the human bowels. This is especially important for women who have a short urethra which is in close proximity of the anus.

It is also more likely to occur in clients who remain in bed. The bottom sheet can be the vehicle of bacterial transfer. In addition, there may be stasis of urine so that the bacteria are not flushed out naturally. The passage of any instrument, such as a catheter into the bladder, can introduce infection.

Following are ways to help prevent urinary infections:

- Using good personal (especially perineal and urethral) hygiene

- Regularly changing bed sheets

- Avoiding an obstruction of the flow of urine out of a catheter

- Safeguarding against backflow of urine from a catheter bag back into the bladder (by ensuring that the catheter bag and tubing are below the level of the client's bladder)

Urine is usually sterile, although bacteria that gain access to the urinary tract can grow successfully. Urinary infection is characterised by the urine being cloudy and having a fishy smell, and there is frequency and urgency of passing urine. On urine testing, there may be protein and blood in the urine (see Module 7).

Exercise 6.36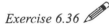

Principles of Care

The principles of care for an individual who has an infection include rest, hygiene, diet, and skin care.

Rest is an important part of the treatment of any illness because the illness will cause the respiratory rate, pulse rate, and temperature to rise. In order to prevent further strain on the body's resources, peace and quiet should be provided to enable maximum rest.

Hygiene is important when high temperatures cause profuse sweating and a lot of discomfort. The individual may need several washes a day, in addition to a daily bath or bed bath.

Oral hygiene is important because the increased temperature, sweating, and raised respiratory rates can cause the person to become dehydrated and the mouth to become very dry and dirty. This is especially true when the infection causes lesions to the mouth and lips.

Fluid balance needs to be monitored, especially when there is profuse sweating, diarrhoea, or vomiting. The dehydration, in combination with an electrolyte (e.g., sodium-potassium) imbalance, can be life-threatening. To maintain fluid balance, a normal, healthy adult needs to ingest at least 2,500 mls or more each day to make up for the fluids lost in urine, faeces, perspiration, and respiration.

Diet can be supplemented with protein and vitamin supplements when the client has lost his or her appetite. When the temperature starts to fall, a light diet should be commenced.

Skin care is very important, especially when the infection causes lesions which are very itchy and the client is sweating. Also, when necessary, pressure areas can be protected by regular turning of the client.

Exercise 6.37

Specimens and Measurement

Guidelines relating to specimen collection and physical measurements can be found in Module 4,

Parts 5 and 6. The information available in those modules can be used as a basis for teaching the correct technique and relevant theory relating to specimen collection and physical measurement that a client or carer would like to undertake independently. You should also search for more comprehensive teaching resources that might be available locally (e.g., leaflets, booklets, teaching packs). If unsure, ask an appropriate member of the care team for advice.

When a client or carer agrees to collect and test specimens or take physical measurements, the level of supervision provided should ensure the following:

- The immediate area is appropriately prepared for the procedure to be undertaken (e.g., windows closed, curtains or screens drawn, the necessary equipment and materials are available and close at hand).

- Appropriate cross-infection precautions are taken (e.g., hand washing before and after the procedure, correct aseptic technique, appropriate disposal of clinical waste).

- The individual undertaking the procedure uses the correct technique at an appropriate place and time, according to the plan of care.

- The client or carer is given appropriate feedback on his or her performance. The emphasis should be on praising the individual who does well and providing guidance when mistakes are made. Try not to be over-critical, and do not be afraid to step in if the client/carer is struggling or appears to be about to do something silly (e.g., use a urinalysis stick that has been contaminated by being dropped onto the floor).

- If the timing and interpretation of the measurements are incorrect, the client or carer should be encouraged to repeat the measurement (as long as this does not cause unnecessary suffering for the client, and the client is in full agreement).

- Changes in the client's condition can be identified, the likely causes ascertained, and appropriate action taken which accords with the care plan. This includes seeking advice and support when the need arises.

- When the agreed plan of care highlights the need to maintain records, the carer or client should be encouraged/assisted to complete the documentation accurately, legibly, and completely. Records will also need to be stored in a safe place.

The following are examples of specimen collections and physical measurements that a client or carer may want to take on:

- Blood specimen collection and analysis
- Urine specimen collection and analysis
- Faeces, sputum, and exudate specimen collection
- Temperature, pulse, and respiration measurements
- Blood pressure measurements
- Weight, height, and girth measurements
- Peak flow measurements
- Fluid balance measurements

Exercise 6.38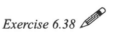

Interpreting the Results

The results of specimen testing and physical measurements need to be interpreted in the light of other information.

Age can affect results. A young child does not have the same resting blood pressure as an elderly person.

"Normal" results for one individual may not be normal for another. There can be quite wide ranges of normal readings (e.g., two healthy, 30-year-old women of the same height and weight may have very different pulse rates).

Known chronic illnesses are likely to give abnormal readings which are "normal" for that person (e.g.,

a client who has chronic obstructive chest disease having a continuously high respiration count).

Extraneous factors can cause "false" reading (e.g., the client who is stressed leading to significant increases in pulse and blood pressure).

Blood Glucose Testing

When a capillary sample of blood has been taken (e.g., from the finger), the normal ranges are below 6.7 mmol/l (fasting blood sugar) or below 11.1 mmol/l (random blood sugar).

Urinalysis

Multistix reagent strips are the most commonly used form of urinalysis. Care must be taken, though, that each square is read at the set time so that the following interpretations can be made:

- Glucose: Read at 30 seconds—results range from negative to ++++. Unless the client is diabetic, glucose is not usually present in urine.

- Bilirubin: Read at 30 seconds—results range from negative to +++. Bilirubin is not usually present in the urine unless the client has jaundice or certain types of anaemia.

- Ketones: Read at 40 seconds—results range from negative to 16. Small amounts of ketones can sometimes be seen in the urine of a person who is dieting, and, higher levels are seen in the urine of clients who have uncontrolled diabetes.

- Specific gravity: Read at 45 seconds—results range from 1.000 to 1.030. The specific gravity of urine is dependent on the strength of the urine. Very low specific gravities can be seen in the urine of people who have drank a lot of water and in some types of kidney disease. Very high specific gravities can be seen in the urine of people who are dehydrated and in other types of kidney disease.

- Blood: Read at 60 seconds—results range from negative to large. Blood is not normally seen in the urine unless there is an infection or a bleed somewhere within the urinary tract.

- pH: Read at 60 seconds—results range from 5 - 8.5. This indicates the acidity of the urine.

- Protein: Read at 60 seconds—results range from negative to +++. Small amounts of protein can sometimes be seen in the normal urine. Large amounts are usually indicative of urinary tract infection and/or kidney damage.

- Urobilinogen: Read at 60 seconds—results range from 3-16 μmol/l (normal range) to 33-131 μmol/l (abnormal range). The abnormal range is usually only seen in clients who have jaundice or anaemia.

Exercise 6.39

Temperature, Pulse, and Respiration

The average ranges of **temperature** measurements in degrees Celsius are:

- oral   36-37°C
- axillary   35.5-36.5°C

A *pyrexia* is a temperature above 37.5°C. It is usually caused by an infection. A *hypothermia* is a temperature below 35°C. It is usually caused by being exposed to a cold environment.

The box below lists normal **pulse** rates. Note that rates decrease with age.

Age	Approximate Range	Average
Newborn	120-160	140
1-12 mos.	80-140	120
12 mos.- 2 yrs.	80-130	110
2-6 yrs.	75-120	100
6-12 yrs.	75-110	95
Adolescent	60-100	80
Adult	60-100	80

Normal Pulse Rates Per Minute

Adults average 16-20 **respirations** per minute. The *peak flow* for a normal, healthy adult is usually around 4,800 ml. A high peak flow can be achieved by an athlete. A low peak flow is indicative of acute or chronic respiratory disease (e.g., asthma).

Blood Pressure

The box below lists **blood pressure** measurements. Note that rates increase from birth to adolescence.

Age	Average Normal BP	Upper Limits of Normal BP
1 yr.	95/65	Unknown
6-9 yrs.	100/65	119/79
10-13 yrs.	110/65	124/84
14-17 yrs.	120/80	134/89
Adult	120-80	139/89

Average and Upper Limits of Blood Pressure

Hypotension (low blood pressure) in adults is usually defined as systolic blood pressure below 100 mm Hg. Apart from when there is shock, in most cases this condition is not a major problem.

Hypertension is defined as a consistent elevation of systolic blood pressure above normal. A temporary raised blood pressure may be due to physical exertion, emotions, stress, or fever. A persistently high blood pressure is a common problem for approximately one-third of the population who are over 50 years of age.

Exercise 6.40

Medications

Guidelines can be found in Module 4, Part 3, relating to the administration of a wide variety of medications by all the major routes (e.g., oral medicines; inhaled medicines; eye, nasal preparations and ear preparations; vaginal and rectal preparations; topical preparations).

Exercise 6.41

The information available in Module 4 can be used as a basis for teaching the correct technique and relevant theory relating to client self-medication or the administration of medications by a carer. You should also search for more comprehensive teaching resources that might be available locally (e.g., leaflets, booklets, teaching packs). If unsure, ask an appropriate member of the care team for advice.

Whether the client is a patient in a hospital ward or based at home, it is assumed that the client is allowed to retain all prescribed medications, and that the client or carer is responsible for ensuring that they are administered at the appropriate time. Therefore, a client who was taking medication prior to admission to hospital, should take the drugs at the same time he or she would take them at home. This is important in long-term medication as a change in the time of administration could cause an altered physiological response to the medication.

The overall aim of medication is to achieve a satisfactory therapeutic response. This can only be achieved if the client or carer complies with the prescribed medication. This includes how the medication should be safely administered and the reasons why the medication is needed. When the client or carer does not understand the reasons for the medication, this can result in mistakes of timing, frequency, and dosage, especially when the drug regime is complicated.

Therefore, when the administration of medications is being carried out by a client or carer, the level of supervision provided should ensure the following:

- The immediate area is appropriately prepared for the administration of medications (e.g., the necessary equipment and materials are available and to hand, where necessary privacy is ensured).

- Appropriate cross-infection precautions are taken (e.g., hand washing before and after the administration of medication, appropriate disposal of clinical waste).

- The individual undertaking the procedure has the necessary competence and confidence to administer the medication correctly (e.g., at an appropriate place and time, according to the prescription).

- The client or carer is given appropriate feedback on his or her performance. The emphasis should be on praising the individual who does well and providing guidance when a mistake is made. Try not to be over-critical and do not be afraid to step in if the client/carer is struggling or appears to be about to do something silly (e.g., trying to administer a tablet that has been contaminated by being dropped onto the floor).

- When significant changes in the client's condition are noticed, the likely causes are identified, and appropriate action taken which accords with the care plan. This includes the client/carer being aware of drug side effects and the consequences of over- and under-medication. It is expected that the client/carer will seek advice and/or support when the need arises.

- When the agreed plan of care highlights the need to maintain records, the carer or client should be encouraged to complete any necessary documentation accurately, legibly, and completely. The records should be kept in a safe place.

- Individuals who wish to use home remedies in conjunction with the medication that has been prescribed are encouraged to seek advice from the doctor in case the home remedy affects the action of the prescribed medication.

- Medication is not "passed around" or shared with others.

There are different types and levels of supervision and support that can be provided for clients and carers who are administering medications. This can range from direct supervision (being physically present whilst the medication is being administered) to indirect supervision (only visiting the client/carer occasionally or being available at the other end of a telephone for advice and support in an emergency or crisis).

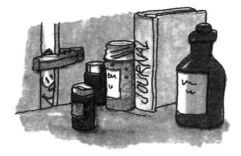

Problems with Medications

A number of problems can occur when medications are administered by clients and/or their carers. Some individuals have *memory problems* and may become confused, especially if there are many medications to be administered. Following are ways to overcome problems:

- Supplying medications in separate bottles, labelled specifically for the client. If prescribed by a hospital pharmacy, the labels should have all the usual instructions as would be provided by a community-based pharmacist (e.g., drug name, route, timing, and dosage).

- Ensuring that the client/carer is given an explanation of the use, action, and side effects of the medication, at an appropriate pace and level, using language that can be easily understood. If necessary, this can be written down to help the client/carer remember.

- Encouraging the client/carer to maintain accurate records of medications administered, or not administered, for any reason

- Retrieving old medications from clients to prevent confusion with any new drugs that have been prescribed

- Providing clients/carers with commercially-produced medicine boxes (often referred to as monitored dosage systems). These should have compartments for the days of the week and further divisions for individual doses within each day

Manual dexterity can result in clients having great difficulty in getting access to medication because of the packaging (e.g., blister packs and childproof tops). This problem can be overcome by providing alternative bottle tops with wing tips that are easy to open. Liquid medications can be administered by syringe rather than risking spillage when using a spoon.

Vision problems can be overcome by ensuring that the printing on bottles is large enough to be read by the client/carer or by providing commercial medicine boxes that have Braille markings.

Storage can be a problem. In a hospital, this should ideally be within a locked drawer, within the client's locker, that is only accessed by the client. In the community, this needs to be in a place (preferably locked) where children and others cannot get access to the medications. Ensure that medications are stored appropriately (e.g., at correct temperature, out of direct sunlight).

The client/carer should be encouraged to check *expiry dates*. All medication that is out of date should be appropriately disposed of (e.g., flushed down the toilet).

When medication is *refused* by the client or *contaminated* (e.g., dropped on the floor), this should be carefully charted. The person providing supervision needs to know from the amount of medication that remains, whether or not the client has been receiving the medication. When a refusal of medication can have serious consequences (e.g., insulin by a diabetic, tranquillisers by a potentially aggressive person), the carer should seek advice immediately.

The client/carer will need to know what to do when he or she has run out of medication. This includes knowing how to get a repeat prescription at short notice and having an arrangement for ensuring that someone can get the medications from the pharmacy for the client.

Summary

An important aspect of your job is helping others to help themselves. This includes assisting clients in finding information about available services and facilities in the community. Enable clients to administer their financial affairs—budgeting, making payments, claiming and collecting benefits and allowances.

Promote independence by helping clients to undertake their own health care needs, whenever possible. Calm their fears, explain procedures, build their confidence, and discuss what to do when there is a problem.

Check Your Knowledge and Understanding

1. An elderly gentleman is living at home with his daughter and son-in-law. He has just been put on the waiting list for a hip replacement, but locally the waiting list is very long. It is expected to be at least 12 months before he has his hip replaced. Unfortunately, the gentleman is rather obese, and he has become wheelchair bound because of the pain in his hips when walking. This is causing a lot of strain on the family. What would you recommend that the family do about this situation?

   a) Phone the consultant to see if he is willing to allow the gentleman to "jump the queue."

   b) Complain bitterly to the general practitioner, and demand that the gentleman is "pushed up" the waiting list.

   c) Look around for an appropriate residential home that can care for the gentleman until he has his hip replaced.

   d) Telephone the Health Information Service to identify a hospital in the region that has a shorter waiting list for hip replacements, and then request that the general practitioner arrange for the gentleman to go there for his hip operation.

2. You have an elderly relative who has recently moved from a residential care home to a nursing home as he has become more dependent on others for this care. The nursing home staff have a set routine, and they have made it clear that they would prefer you not to provide care for the relative when you visit him on a regular basis. Which of the following would you do?

   a) Comply with the wishes of the care staff, as long as your relative appears to be receiving good care.

   b) Negotiate a plan of care with the care team and the relatives that includes your input into the provision of care.

   c) Make a formal complaint to the nursing home manager about the inappropriateness of an enforced routine and your exclusion from care involvement.

   d) Immediately withdraw your relative from the home.

3. One of your clients is heavily in debt. He approaches you for advice about the possibility of obtaining additional benefits and/or allowances. Which of the following would you do?

   a) Undertake a personal budgeting exercise, with the client's permission, to enable you to compare his income to his expenditure. Then plan the way forward.

   b) Provide him with appropriate advice and support so that he can apply for a Crisis Loan from the Social Fund.

   c) Inform him that if he spent less on tobacco and gambling, he wouldn't be in so much debt.

   d) Offer to help him get a loan at your bank so that he can pay off his debts as cheaply as possible.

4. A client has been taken shopping for some new clothes by a member of care staff. They return with several items of shopping, but the receipts are missing. The member of care staff says he has, somehow, lost them. He says that he has spent all but 47 pence of the client's £250. Unfortunately, there doesn't appear to be £250 worth of clothes in the bags. Which of the following would you do?

   a) Accept the explanation of the member of care staff, but remind him about the need to save receipts next time, as specified in the organisation's financial procedures.

   b) Inform your manager about the situation so that he can take the appropriate disciplinary measures because the organisation's financial procedures have not been followed.

   c) Have a quiet word with the member of staff and the client, if possible, to find out which shops they have purchased the clothes from. Then go and visit the shops to check up on what was actually spent and to see if you can get duplicate receipts.

   d) Confront the member of staff with the fact that you suspect him of stealing money from the client.

5. During a discussion with a client, she discloses that she has been receiving benefits and allowances for more than six months to which she is not entitled. What should you do?

   a) Demand that she immediately stops claiming benefits and allowances to which she is not entitled.

   b) Insist that she quickly pays back all the monies that she has defrauded from the system and stops claiming the benefits to which she is not entitled.

   c) Maintain confidentiality, and allow the client to continue to claim the additional benefits and allowances to which she is not entitled.

   d) Inform her that you will have to pass on this information to the appropriate authorities.

6. One of your regular clients telephones you in tears, saying that she cannot cope any longer. She has been providing quite a high level of physical care for her husband since he has been discharged home from hospital after having a stroke. The client says that her husband has become rather confused and verbally abusive over the last few days. She also thinks that he may have developed a urinary infection because the urine in the drainage bag is very cloudy. Which of the following would you do?

   a) Provide some "telephone counselling" to the client whilst reassuring her that she is coping well and telling her to contact her general practitioner for advice.

   b) Promise to call at the house within the next 10 days to assess the situation and provide further reassurance.

   c) Leave a message for the client's general practitioner so that he knows about the problem.

   d) Promise the client that you will visit her that day so that an initial assessment of the situation can be made.

7. A disabled, elderly woman has been admitted to your care facility for mobilisation after having a minor heart attack. She is being prepared for discharge back into the community where she lives alone in sheltered accommodation. The doctor wants her to continue to take the same blood pressure and sleeping tablets that she usually takes at home. She has a supply of these tablets with her and insists that she is able to administer her own medication without interference from others. The woman is very alert and does not suffer fools gladly. Client self-medication has not been tried within this area before, and some of the care workers are not very keen on this idea. If it was your decision, what would you do?

a) Allow the woman to self-medicate, but ask her to keep the medications in a locked section within her bedside locker.

b) In addition to "a," insist that the woman fills out a chart indicating that she has taken the right medication in the right way, at the right time. In addition, you will count her remaining tablets on a regular basis to ensure that she is correctly administering her medication.

c) Remove the tablets from the woman's possession, and add them to those held in the drugs trolley so that the woman can give herself her own medication when the medicine round is carried out.

d) Remove the tablets from the woman's possession, informing her that self-medication is not allowed within this care facility.

Module 7

Need-to-know words:

- alimentary canal
- anus
- bile pigments
- cellulose
- colon
- colostomy
- Crohn's disease
- cystitis
- diuretic
- encopresis
- enema
- enuresis
- excretion
- flatus
- haemorrhoids
- micturition
- nocturia
- paralytic ileus
- perianal
- peristalsis
- prostate gland
- quadriplegia
- roughage
- sacral area
- sphincter
- ureter
- urethra

Providing Physical Comfort and Enabling Continence

Enable others to achieve physical comfort.

Objectives:

- Describe the relevant anatomy and physiology linked to urinary and bowel elimination.
- Outline common problems of elimination.
- Explain how individuals can be helped to maintain continence.
- Highlight the effects of incontinence on the lives of clients and their families.
- Describe a range of incontinence aids and their uses.
- Outline how to help clients overcome the problems caused by their incontinence.
- Outline how the dangers to client and carer can be minimised during manual handling.
- Demonstrate a range of techniques that are used for the manual handling of clients.
- Demonstrate the correct usage of a variety of manual handling aids.
- Explain how pressure sores can be prevented.
- Demonstrate the correct use of pressure-relieving equipment.

Module 7 Introduction

Module 7 relates to two units of the level 3 NVQ/ SVQ Award in Care:

Unit Z12: **Contribute to the management of client continence** is an option group B unit. It consists of two elements of competence:

- Z12.1 Encourage clients to maintain continence.

- Z12.2 Support clients in the management of continence.

Unit Z7: **Contribute to the movement and handling of clients to maximise their physical comfort** is an option group B unit. It consists of three elements of competence:

- Z7.1 Prepare clients and environments for moving and handling.

- Z7.2 Assist clients to move from one position to another.

- Z7.3 Assist clients to prevent and minimise the adverse effects of pressure.

Part 1: Enabling People to Manage Incontinence (Z12)

Support others to manage their own elimination needs.

In the normal expectation of a lifetime, it is acceptable for all babies to be incontinent. Their bladders and bowels fill and empty automatically. By the age of three years, it is expected that most children will be fully continent during the day; and by the age of five years, most will also be continent during the night. Children are expected to learn the feeling of bladder and bowel fullness and to link this to the need to use the toilet or hold the contents until a toilet is available.

Good bladder and bowel control are normally expected to be maintained throughout life, although it is accepted that in old age there may be some degenerative changes in the body which affect personal elimination. There is also a range of abnormal elimination patterns which must be managed by some people (e.g., the multiple handicapped child who will always be doubly incontinent; the mother who has had several babies and now finds herself becoming incontinent; the person who has had an operation and now finds himself with a colostomy). It is essential that you have some knowledge of relevant anatomy and physiology before you attempt to help a client who has continence problems.

Exercise 7.1 🖉

Bowel Function

The colon is approximately 1.5 metres in length. Its main functions include the following:

- Eliminate the waste products of digestion by propelling faeces towards the anus.
- Produce mucus to lubricate the faecal mass.
- Absorb fluid and electrolytes (the colon absorbs about two litres of water in 24 hours).
- Store faeces.
- Synthesise vitamins B and K through the action of bacterial micro-organisms.

Faeces consists of the unabsorbed end-products of digestion (e.g., bile pigments, cellulose, bacteria, mucus, inorganic matter). It is normally semi-solid in consistency and contains about 70 percent water.

The faeces moves through the colon towards the anus via peristalsis. If there is not enough roughage in the faeces, it moves slowly through the colon and additional water is absorbed. If there are delays in expelling the faeces, even more water is absorbed which makes the faeces even harder and more difficult to expel.

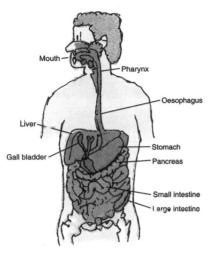

Digestive Tract

Faeces normally remain in the sigmoid colon until the person feels the stimulus to defaecate. The stimulus varies with individuals according to habit, as it can be controlled by conscious effort. After a few minutes, the stimulus disappears and may not return for several hours.

In response to the stimulus, the faeces move into the rectum, which is very sensitive to rises in pressure. This will stimulate the desire to defaecate. A coordinated reflex, which includes a wave of peristalsis, then empties the bowel. To release and stop the flow of faeces and prevent leakage of faeces from the rectum, there is a **sphincter** situated between the rectum and the anus. The sphincter is important in controlling the passage of faeces and flatus as it can be consciously controlled by an individual.

In addition, the rectum passes through the rear portion of the **pelvic floor muscles.** These support the contents of the abdominal cavity and have a function in controlling the release and flow of faeces and flatus from the body. When a woman has a baby, the birth can stretch the pelvic floor muscles and leave a weakness. Both the sphincter and the pelvic floor muscles can be strengthened by exercise to provide better bowel control.

Finally, the bowel function is controlled by a nerve communication system between bowels and brain. Stretch receptors in the sigmoid colon send a mes-

sage to the brain to inform the person of the need to defaecate. A message can then be sent from the brain to the sphincter for it to relax so the contents of the bowel can be emptied at an appropriate time and place. Any disturbance of this two-way communication system at any level can significantly affect bowel function.

To ensure normal function of the bowels, a person usually needs a diet that contains enough fibre and water and sufficient exercise to stimulate the bowels. This needs to be accompanied by easy access to appropriate toilet facilities in which a client can feel comfortable. Therefore, whenever possible, bedpans should be avoided as they are embarrassing to use.

It is a myth that a daily bowel evacuation is needed to remain healthy. The first objective in assessing a person's bowel habits must be to discover what is "normal" for that person. For some people twice a week is normal; for others, twice a day.

Exercise 7.2 ✏

The Urinary Tract

Urine is produced by the **kidneys**. The kidneys act like a filtration system for the blood. A healthy person on a normal balanced diet will produce between two to three pints (1200-1800 ml) of urine every 24 hours.

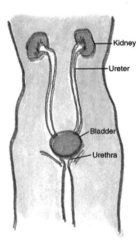

The urine passes from the kidney, down the **ureters** and into the bladder. At the bladder end of the ureters is a type of valve. This ensures that urine can pass into the bladder and prevents backflow.

The **bladder** collects the urine from the upper urinary tract, stores it, and then empties it out through the urethra to remove urine from the body. The wall of the bladder is a mix of muscle and elastic tissue. This can act like a balloon to store urine, and then contract to empty it. A small bladder has to empty frequently, whilst a large bladder does not need to be emptied quite so often.

Urine escapes from the bladder by passing along the urethra. A female urethra is short (not much more than one inch in length). A man's urethra tends to be much longer, as it has to reach to the end of the penis. Also it has to pass through the **prostate gland** as it leaves the bladder. This gland tends to increase in size with age and can interfere with the flow of urine.

To release and stop the flow of urine and prevent leakage of urine from the bladder, there are two **sphincters** situated where the urethra leaves the bladder. Both sphincters are important in controlling the passage of urine, although only one (voluntary sphincter) can be consciously controlled by an individual. In addition, the urethra passes through the front part of the **pelvic floor muscles.** These support the contents of the abdominal cavity and have a function in controlling the release and flow of urine from the body. Also, an increase in intra-abdominal pressure can be used by an individual to put pressure on the wall of the bladder so that urine is voided more quickly.

Finally, urinary function is controlled by a nerve communication system between lower urinary system and brain. Stretch receptors in the bladder send a message to the brain to inform the person of the need to pass urine. A message can then be sent from the brain to the internal sphincter for it to relax so the contents of the bladder can be emptied at an appropriate time and place by the relaxation of the voluntary sphincter. Any disturbance of this two-way communication system at any level can significantly affect the elimination of urine.

Urine enters the bladder in a steady continuous trickle from the upper urinary tract. A healthy bladder should hold between a half to one pint of urine. The largest quantity is usually stored after a night's sleep. Normally, during the day, the bladder should need to be emptied approximately every five hours, although there can be great variations in these figures.

The sensation of fullness in the bladder usually signals the need to pass urine. This signal is not always reliable. The sound of running water or the sight of a toilet may make a person feel the need to pass urine. In contrast, a person may feel the need to pass urine and become distracted, resulting in the need to urinate to pass for a while.

Exercise 7.3 🖉

The urine that is excreted can appear clear like water or be a dark yellow colour, depending on the concentration of the urine. Whatever colour it is, urine should be clear, contain no debris, and should not have an unpleasant smell.

Some beverages, such as tea and coffee, have a mild diuretic effect which results in the kidneys producing more urine. The increased output of urine results in the bladder needing to be emptied more often. Alcoholic drinks have a similar effect.

Any (apparent) change in pattern and type of elimination should be checked with the client and reported immediately to an appropriate member of the care team. Urine and faeces can be accompanied by blood, mucus, pus, etc. Therefore, remember to use Universal Precautions when dealing with all waste products (see Module 3, Part 2).

Bowel Problems

Diarrhoea can be defined as an abnormal increase in the frequency, quantity, and fluid content of faeces which can be accompanied by urgency, perianal and/ or abdominal discomfort, and incontinence. The main treatment is to identify and treat the cause of the diarrhoea. *Acute diarrhoea* can be caused by food poisoning, bowel-irritating diets (e.g., excessive spices, fruit, beer), drugs (e.g., antibiotics), and allergies to certain food constituents. *Chronic diarrhoea* can be caused by diseases of the colon (e.g., cancer, inflammatory bowel disease), and inflammatory diseases of the bowel (e.g., Crohn's disease).

The main danger is that a person can become very dehydrated due to diarrhoea, especially if that individual is also vomiting. If dehydration starts to occur, or if you feel that there is an underlying disease that needs treatment, the doctor should be summoned immediately.

Exercise 7.4 🖉

Constipation can be defined as an irregular and infrequent bowel movement associated with the passage of hard, bulky faeces. A client will normally complain of difficulty when defecating, together with pain and discomfort. When someone is severely constipated, the faecal impaction can cause fluid to leak around the sides of the faeces and cause diarrhoea.

To establish that a person is constipated, and to what degree, a rectal examination is needed. This is usually undertaken by a qualified and experienced member of care staff. When a person has a history of becoming constipated, the focus of treatment should be on identifying the cause and the development of a long-term plan to prevent the constipation from occurring. This may include taking more exercise, including more roughage in the diet, and/or drinking more fluids.

Encopresis refers to incontinence of faeces and is usually applied to children who mess their beds at night. It is usually no longer a problem by the time a child is five years old. If it continues, investigations should be undertaken to establish the cause.

Haemorrhoids can make defecation uncomfortable and/or painful. They sometimes remain in the rectum, but can be forced through the anus with the passage of faeces. When this occurs, they usually have to be manhandled back into the rectum. There are a number of problems that can be caused by haemorrhoids. They can drop through the anus during the day and stain underclothes with faeces or blood, and they can make defecation painful.

Usually haemorrhoids can be treated with a proprietary cream which shrinks them. Alternatively, if they become large, they can be injected to shrink them, or they can be surgically removed.

Urinary Problems

The **rate of flow** of urine varies. Some individuals find it very difficult to pass urine anywhere except in their own toilets where they can have quiet and privacy. For other individuals, feelings of apprehensiveness can affect the flow of urine.

Most people can sleep through the night without having to pass urine. However, it is not uncommon, especially for the elderly, to have to pass urine one or more times in the night. This is referred to as **nocturia**. Obviously, this affects the amount and quality of sleep a person gets.

Sexual intercourse can also cause problems for the female, especially if there has been a lack of vaginal lubrication. This can lead to **cystitis,** which makes the bladder very sensitive and leads to frequency and urgency of the need to pass urine.

The most common type of **urinary incontinence** is the one caused by the feeling that the bladder is overflowing and about to burst. It is characterised by people looking uncomfortable, shuffling their feet, crossing and uncrossing their legs, looking for an opportunity to make a discrete exit, whilst they try to "hold on." If a toilet is not found in time, or their legs cannot carry them fast enough, the inevitable leakage of urine occurs. This is called *frequency* or *urge incontinence*. It is often caused by having a small bladder, by the irritation of the bladder wall caused by cystitis, or because an individual has not trained the bladder to hold at least half a pint of urine.

Exercise 7.5 🖉

People instinctively try to control this problem by restricting the amount of fluid that they drink. Often, they will visit the toilet at every available opportunity. In care facilities, clients with mobility problems will need to have some way of calling for help when they feel the urge to use the toilet.

For those people who have not trained their bladders to hold at least half a pint of urine, this problem can be overcome by a bladder retraining programme. This requires the individual to slowly increase the amounts of time between visits to the toilet, or the amount of time between first feeling the need to use the toilet and actually using the toilet.

An **atonic bladder** occurs when there has been damage to the sensory nerve pathway between the bladder and the spinal cord. This usually results in the absence of, or reduced sensation of, bladder fullness. The outcome is that normal micturition does not occur. The urine has to be manually emptied in conjunction with the use of the abdominal muscles. Sometimes the bladder can become over-distended, leading to overflow incontinence. Occasionally, frequency of micturition can be a feature when some degree of sensation is present.

In **bladder instability,** there is the loss of the signal from the brain which inhibits emptying of the bladder. This results in the reflex arc of the message of fullness of the bladder being sent to the brain and the brain sending a message to the internal sphincter to relax. This situation results in poor bladder capacity, which is accompanied by frequency and urgency. It has been suggested that most older people suffer from some degree of bladder instability.

Stress incontinence occurs when the urethral sphincters are not working properly and allow urine to leak, especially during periods of physical exertion which raise intra-abdominal pressure (e.g., lifting, bending, coughing, sneezing, or laughing). This is more common in females, especially those who have some damage to pelvic floor muscles from a prolonged childbirth. For many people who are otherwise fit, healthy, and active, continence can often be restored by retraining and strengthening bladder control.

Outflow obstruction usually involves the neck of the bladder. The bladder responds by increasing the force of its contractions in an attempt to overcome the obstruction. If not rectified, an atonic bladder and a damaged upper urinary tract can be the result. It is typified by the elderly man with chronic retention of urine, although this problem is occasionally seen in women. There may be hesitancy when a person consciously wants to pass urine but experiences a delay in initiating the flow. Other symptoms may include:

- Involuntary leakage of urine
- Frequency
- Urgency
- Infection
- Poor urine flow, even when straining hard
- Dribbling after micturition

In men, the cause is usually enlargement of the prostate gland, tumours in the bladder neck, or sexually transmitted disease.

Infections of the urinary tract can be a precipitating factor in causing incontinence. Urinary infection is more common in females because of the shorter length of the urethra. Usually, the symptoms include urgency and frequency, painful micturition, high temperature, and pain. The condition may require treatment with an appropriate antibiotic. The following advice can be given to women who get recurrent infections and cystitis:

- Check for an incorrectly fitted diaphragm which can cause pressure during sexual intercourse and cause an infection.

- Be aware that spermicide on some condoms can cause an allergic reaction.

- Increase fluid intake by at least 500 mls per day as this can wash out low-grade infections.

- Take potassium citrate when the symptoms of infection occur. This is available from the pharmacy without a prescription. Three grams taken in water, three times per day can get rid of a mild infection by making the urine alkaline. Alternatively, drink cranberry juice (at least three glasses per day) to make the urine alkaline. (As a preventive measure, drink one glass of cranberry juice daily.)

Enuresis usually refers to a child wetting the bed. This should not be a problem by the time a child is five years old. If it continues, investigations should be undertaken to establish the cause. Treatment can include the use of drugs which are given to act on the smooth muscle of the bladder so that there is less likelihood of leakage.

Exercise 7.6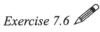

Problems Affecting Bowel Function

Drugs which are taken for illnesses can affect bladder and/or bowel function. One example is diuretics which substantially increase urine output and can result in urge incontinence if there are mobility problems. Other drugs used to treat problems (e.g., pain, respiratory, cardiac, and psychological) can affect smooth muscle in other parts of the body causing frequency/retention of urine and/or constipation/diarrhoea. For example, opiates which are used to combat severe pain frequently cause constipation and severe faecal impaction by lowering bowel motility.

Psychological factors can have a bearing on continence. Incontinence is sometimes a feature of stress or emotional breakdown and may follow a sudden life crisis such as a traumatic illness or bereavement. An impairment of mental functioning can also result in incontinence. Considerable improvements can be achieved by continence management. This is especially true for elderly people who become incontinent due to the confusion and disorientation of being moved into a new care facility. Careful explanation, reassurance, and a review of the client's drug regime can do much to alleviate the problem.

Geographical factors pertain to the surroundings in which a person may live. The following geographical factors may not be conducive to maintaining or regaining continence:

- The toilets are not easily accessible or available.

- The client has mobility problems making it difficult to get to the toilet quickly.

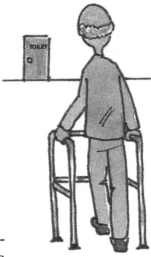

- The client is positioned a long way from the nearest toilet.

- The physical environment is a problem (e.g., stairs).

Exercise 7.7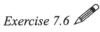

Managing Incontinence

All health authorities employ one or more people who have specific responsibilities for the provision of counselling, advice, and treatment for continence problems (e.g., continence advisor, stoma therapist). Be aware of all the resources that are available in your district to help with the maintenance of continence and the management of incontinence, and be clear about your role in helping people with these problems.

Incontinence is a widespread problem. For example, it has been estimated that more than three million people in the United Kingdom suffer from incontinence to a greater or lesser degree. Faecal incontinence is less common than urinary incontinence.

For many people, incontinence is an embarrassing subject. Uncontrollable leaks of urine or faeces at inconvenient times and in inconvenient places is a major cause of concern. Therefore, many people who suffer this burden will try to ignore the problem, at least initially, rather than take positive steps to try and improve the situation. Usually, the problem is only recognised when, in utter frustration and despair, a person realises that he or she can no longer hide the truth from others.

Exercise 7.8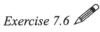

The main reasons an individual may choose not to seek out professional help for a continence problem include the following (Moody, 1990):

- **Fear** of not being in control and able to manage independently; fear of embarrassment or recrimination if the individual makes a mess

171

- **Embarrassment** at the need for help to eliminate waste products; embarrassment at having to hide the use of incontinence aids and find ways to dispose of them

- **Shame** of being incontinent and feeling dirty

- **Denial** due to fear, embarrassment, guilt, and shame can cause the individual to deny there is a problem, even in the face of overwhelming evidence (e.g., a continually wet patch on the trousers)

- **Resignation** due to feelings of hopelessness and helplessness and the perceived inevitability of the situation

A sudden and unexpected loss of self-control resulting in incontinence is a humiliating experience. Many people suffer in silence, concealing the problem, even from spouses and/or doctors. They have fears and worries about the future, and they are concerned about having the pleasures of life severely modified to cope with the problem. This can result in depression.

In reality, elimination needs will start to control the individual's life. The problem dominates the person's thoughts and causes a great deal of anguish and anxiety. Any excursion from the home has to be meticulously planned to overcome needs, such as access to toilets, use and disposal of incontinence pads, and the need for changes of clothing.

These needs require a significant increase in the amount of planning and baggage required for all outings and holidays. This problem tends to reduce the amount of socialising with family and friends. It results in the client having severe difficulties in maintaining and developing meaningful relationships, resulting in desolation and despair. A knock-on effect occurs with the rest of the family as the whole family's outings will tend to be curtailed and reduced in frequency. This can cause resentment.

A further problem that is caused by incontinence is linked to available finances. Many health authorities expect clients to contribute to the cost of their continence aids. This can make life very difficult for those families who have low disposable incomes.

A positive attitude demonstrated by the care worker can go a long way to overcoming the shame, anger, hostility, or apathy shown by some clients. It is essential that the care worker avoids giving the impression of being patronising, condescending, or revolted by a client's incontinence.

The main aim of incontinence management, therefore, is to support the client in resuming a "normal" lifestyle (e.g., the type of lifestyle undertaken by the person before he became incontinent).

Exercise 7.9 🖉

Monitoring Elimination

The assessment of a client who is incontinent may involve a number of health and social care professionals. It is important, therefore, that each is aware of the role and functions of the others to prevent duplication and omission of aspects of assessment and treatment.

When dealing with clients who have continence problems, the first thing that usually needs to be done is to help them get over their embarrassment when talking about toileting and continence problems. Provide them with a better understanding of how the human body works in relation to elimination.

The embarrassment about toileting can be seen in the language that people use. There are many different expressions for emptying the bladder. For example, most people will not use the terms micturition or urination; they will tend to use more colloquial terms such as "passing water," "taking a leak," "doing a number one," or "spending a penny." There are also many different expressions for emptying the bowel (e.g., "having a dump," "doing a number two," "dropping off a package," or "having a crap").

When talking to clients about their elimination problems, it is important that you talk to them at a level and speed, and using words that they understand.

Therefore, you will need to choose your words carefully to ensure that an individual client understands and is not offended or embarrassed.

Exercise 7.10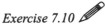

A full assessment of continence will include asking questions about all the following issues:

- What is the general medical history?
- Has the diet and fluid intake been assessed?
- Does the client have a balanced diet with adequate fluids?
- Does the client have easy access to a toilet?
- Does the client have the physical capabilities to dress, undress, and use a toilet?
- Are toileting aids used?
- What are the client's and family's attitudes to the continence problem?
- When did the incontinence commence, and was it connected with any single event?
- Are incontinence aids being used?
- Passing urine:
  - Is the stream good?
  - Are there dribbles after passing urine?
- Passing faeces:
  - Are there haemorrhoids?
- Passing faeces/urine:
  - Does the output look normal?
  - How often?
  - How much?
  - Any leakage?
  - Any pain or discomfort?
  - Is there leakage on coughing, sneezing, or physical exertion?
  - Can the client hold on, or does the toilet have to be accessed quickly?
- At night:
  - Does the client have to use the toilet?
  - How many times?
  - Is there incontinence?

- Physical examinations:
  - Palpation of the abdomen
  - Genitals, perineum, and anus
  - Residual urine
  - Rectal examination
- Has the urine and/or faeces been tested?
- How does the incontinence affect the client's lifestyle?

Exercise 7.11

Incontinence is always a symptom of an underlying problem rather than a problem in itself. In some care environments a continence score chart may be used (e.g., the Searby Score Chart). This is used to help care providers to easily identify the cause of clients' incontinence problems. It is a simple design, using a scoring system similar to that utilised on the Norton Scale for assessing pressure areas.

Planning Incontinence Care

Some people are incontinent only occasionally or for a short period of time during an illness. Others are likely to have varying degrees of incontinence for the rest of their lives. The leakage of urine and faeces must be controlled so that it affects lifestyles as little as possible and does not damage the skin. A wide range of appliances, treatments, and techniques can be considered. The byword for the continence specialist is that "incontinence can sometimes be cured, usually relieved, and always made more tolerable."

Support should be provided to clients in a way that promotes self-respect, maximises privacy, and is consistent with the plan of care. Whatever method is used to manage an individual's incontinence, people are the most important resource. An individual's strengths and weaknesses will need to be identified so that a plan of

173

care can be established to meet any self-care deficits. In a care facility, few problems should exist in providing this service. But, in the community, these needs have to be met by the family and/or other carers. This can sometimes be difficult when the incontinent family member is resented because of the restrictions on family activities imposed by the incontinence.

The main areas of intervention for individuals who have continence problems include the following:

- Assist the client to eliminate at an appropriate time and place.

- Provide assistance for a client to re-establish "normal" patterns of elimination.

- Teach and advise the client on techniques to promote continence.

- Advise the client on how to adapt food and fluid intake in order to achieve a healthier and more balanced diet.

- Teach the client on how to avoid urinary tract infections.

- Ensure that the side effects of drugs that are having an effect on continence are minimised.

- Provide counselling and support to both the client and the family to overcome any emotional or psychological factors that are adversely affecting the continence problem.

Whatever the plan of care, it needs to be re-assessed at intervals to make sure that the plan, the use of continence aids, and the level of support provided are still appropriate for the client. The emphasis is always on enabling clients to do as much as they can for themselves. This may require careful thought to ensure that clients have easy access to toilets, continence aids, and methods of disposing of, or cleaning, soiled linen and clothing.

Exercise 7.12 🖉

Toilet Facilities

Access to toilets, sanitation, and security can affect toileting needs. Some people do not have easy access to toilets (e.g., narrow doorways, blocked corridors, toilet too high or too low). There can also be problems when individuals are required to use public toilets in the community, especially when there is a lack of privacy and/or they are not sure that the toilet door locks are secure. Access to, and ability to use, toilet paper is an important aspect of toileting if soiled undergarments are to be avoided.

In care facilities, access to toilets should not be a problem, but the thought of having to use communal toilets makes many people feel uncomfortable. The toilets may not seem clean enough or smell nice enough for the clients. The thought of someone using the toilet next to them can make people feel very uncomfortable. This is especially true if that person might be someone of the opposite sex and/or if they can hear and smell everything that is going on next door.

Exercise 7.13 🖉

The problem is exacerbated when commodes, sanichairs, bedpans, and urinals need to be used. Some clients cope very well with this form of toileting. For others, the stress of toileting in this fashion is likely to exacerbate their continence problems, especially when there are problems of moving and positioning a client. It is up to you to negotiate a mutually acceptable solution to toileting problems with the client and/ or the family.

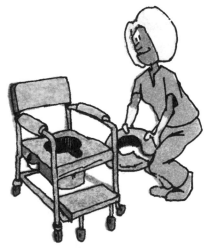

Diet

For some clients who have continence problems, a change of diet is all that is needed to achieve significant improvements. A dietitian can be very helpful in these situations, especially when diet sheets need to be provided to the client.

Some clients drink too much or too little fluid in their daily diet. Sometimes people will drink too little because of lack of motivation. Others deliberately restrict fluids to keep "accidents" to a minimum. Whatever the reason, the lack of fluid reduces the urine outputs and makes the urine very concentrated. The concentrated urine itself can irritate the bladder wall and cause urgency. In addition, the fluid restriction makes constipation more likely to occur.

Occasionally, there is a simple solution to the problem (e.g., advise the client not to drink tea, coffee or alcohol after 6 p.m. to prevent nocturia and/or night-time incontinence). Large amounts of tea and coffee during the day can cause problems for clients who have mobility problems and cannot get to the toilet on time.

In the battle against continence problems, a client usually needs a balanced diet, in the right proportions—fluids, calories, proteins, carbohydrates, fats, roughage, vitamins, and minerals.

Exercise 7.14

Pelvic Floor Exercises

The majority of female clients with mild to moderate stress incontinence can be helped by exercising the muscles of the pelvic floor. These muscles have an active role in supporting the pelvic organs and in helping the sphincters counteract the effects of intra-abdominal pressure.

The strength of the pelvic floor muscles is usually assessed by a health care professional who will insert two fingers into the vagina and ask the client to stop her from pulling her fingers out. The pressure that can be exerted by the client ranges from a momentary twitch to a firm squeeze. Another exercise that is used to strengthen the pelvic floor muscles is to ask the client to stop passing urine in mid-stream. This action also helps the client to learn which muscles to contract.

The success of pelvic floor exercises depends on the client's willingness to establish and maintain a regular exercise programme. The exercises can be un-dertaken whilst the client is sitting, standing, or lying with the legs slightly apart. The muscles of the vaginal and anal passages are clenched for a count of five, and then relaxed. The exercise should be repeated four to five times each hour of the day. The majority of women who have mild to moderate stress incontinence can achieve continence within 12 months by using these exercises. Alternatively, the client can be taught to separately contract the posterior pelvic floor muscles as if preventing flatus from escaping from the bowel, and to contract the anterior pelvic floor muscles as if preventing the flow of urine.

Exercise 7.15

Toilet Training Programmes

The aim of toilet training programmes is for the client to re-establish continence or, at least, minimise incontinence. A training programme is especially effective for clients who forget to go to the toilet and for clients who do not have the mental alertness to know that they should go to the toilet. Each programme must be *individually designed* to meet the needs of a specific client. This technique will go against the grain in some care institutions where there is a single toileting regime that is applied to all clients, regardless of their individual problems.

The first stage of a toilet training programme is to record a baseline in addition to any preliminary continence assessment that has been undertaken. The baseline is an accurate record over a period of at least one week that highlights the client's individual elimination patterns. The baseline should indicate precise times and places of elimination, and whether or not the client was continent. Determine whether there are any health problems (e.g., constipation) that are affecting elimination. If so, these problems must be tackled before the toilet training starts.

The baseline gives you a good idea when a client is likely to want to micturate or defaecate. Once you know that, then you can plan a toileting regime which ensures that the client is at the toilet at the times when he or she is likely to need to use it. For example, if the client usually wets the bed between 7-7.30 a.m., you can ensure a visit to the toilet before 7 a.m. This type of approach can be incorporated within a behavioural plan of care where, for example, a child is rewarded with a sweet when he successfully uses the toilet.

Exercise 7.16 🖎

A **goal plan** is one way to plan care for a client who has continence problems. The plan should include a clear and concise statement concerning a target to be achieved. It should be achievable and measurable, with a clearly specified time limit for its achievement. The plan should be negotiated with the client and other interested parties.

A goal plan will have a series of goals and will detail how those goals are to be achieved. A series of goals for a client who has urgency and frequency might be similar to the box below.

Target Date	Goal
End of Week 1	Hold on for at least five minutes without incontinence before going to the toilet.
End of Week 2	Hold on for 10 minutes without incontinence.
End of Week 3	Hold on for 15 minutes without incontinence.
End of Week 4	Hold on for 30 minutes without incontinence.
End of Week 5	Hold on for one hour without incontinence.
End of Week 6	Hold on for at least two hours without incontinence.

Exercise 7.17 🖎

Incontinence Aids

Protective Pants

Protective pants and pads are for intractable incontinence. They are not a cure for the problem, and there is a danger that an individual may regard them as such, rather than seek help to overcome the root cause of the problem.

The pad that is chosen needs to be capable of absorbing the usual amount of leakage balanced against the preferred size of pad and type of pants that are needed to hold the pad in place, the potential for odours, and the personal preferences of the individual concerned. Following are other factors that need to be taken into consideration:

Protective Pad

- Client mobility and hand dexterity
- Level of alertness, mental stability to change the pad
- Vaginal/urethral discharge which may cause odours
- Type and level of faecal incontinence
- Thoroughness and regularity of hygiene measures taken by the client

Those individuals with urgency and stress incontinence, if the quantity of urine loss is small, **need to have small absorbent pads that can be quickly changed.** A young lady may want small pants that have a floral design. The older man might be quite happy with a Y front style of pants that can hold a pad. A very disabled person, on the other hand, with total incontinence, will require a pad capable of absorbing large amounts of urine and/or faeces.

One common mistake is thinking that several layers of pads will increase the absorbency. This will not work unless the plastic backing sheets of the pads are removed before they are put into place. Another is that large pads necessarily absorb more than small pads. Less bulky pads have been developed which have high absorbency.

Exercise 7.18 🖎

Male Appliances

An **appliance** works very well for most men, as long as they are anatomically suited to the device.

Gross obesity, a retracted penis, or a scrotal hernia may make it impossible to fit a device. Great care needs to be taken in fitting the appliance as it may become too tight and cause swelling of the penis. If it is too large, it can slip off and cause leakage, or the collecting bag may fill with air. It is best if a continence advisor fits these appliances.

A **pubic pressure urinal** is the most complicated appliance to use as it has a number of component parts. It has a number of sizes of sheath diameters and flanges. It is not suitable for people with poor eyesight, limited dexterity, or those who are mentally confused or disoriented. The tip of the urinal is attached to a urine collection bag.

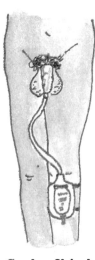

Condom Urinal

The **condom urinal** consists of a special sheath or condom which is attached to a collecting bag. It is designed so that it can be secured to the penis with an adhesive strip. The local skin around the base of the penis should be shaved to ensure that the adhesive does not become stuck to hairs (as this can be painful when the sheath is removed). The end of the sheath is attached to a urine collection bag. The sheath is usually left in place for 24 hours, although some can be left for longer. A client must meet the following criteria before he can have a condom urinal fitted:

- The penis should not be retracted.
- The skin of the penis should not be broken or inflamed (although a barrier cream can be used).
- The individual should not be confused so that he is likely to pull the sheath off.

For **fitting a one-piece self-adhesive penile sheath,** follow these procedures:

1. Measure the size of the penis by using the specially designed measuring device provided by the manufacturer. The circumference of the penis is estimated by placing the device at the base of the penis, ensuring that the size chosen is not too tight or too slack.

Penile Sheath

2. The size of sheath indicated by the measuring device is noted, and then, if possible, the different types of condom urinal systems should be shown to the client so that he can choose one.

3. The penis should be shaved (if hairy), and then washed and dried. No talcs or creams should be applied as this will prevent the sheath from adhering to the penis.

4. Take the sheath from the packet. Then cut a hole in the middle of the packet so that it can be pushed over the penis to the base. This keeps the pubic hair away from the shaft of the penis. Ensure that the foreskin is not retracted during this procedure.

5. Place the penis into the sheath, leaving a one centimeter gap between the tip of the penis and the tip of the sheath. The sheath should be gently unrolled down the length of the penis and firmly secured by pressing the sheath so it adheres to the penis.

6. Remove the protective collar made from the packet, and discard it.

7. Attach the drainage bag to the end of the sheath, and then securely strap the bag to the client's leg.

8. To remove a sheath, simply roll it off the client's penis, and discard it.

Dribble bags are designed for men who have a minor dribble incontinence. The bags generally consist of a disposable plastic bag on a waist band or a waterproof pouch in which to collect the urine.

All appliances have to be washed daily by taking the appliance apart, washing well in warm soapy water, and drying thoroughly. It is usually necessary to have several appliances so that they can be rotated and used.

Great care needs to be taken of the skin when wearing the appliances as they can make the penis, scrotum, and thighs sore. The appliance, when first given, should be worn for slowly increasing lengths of time until it can be well tolerated. Every time the appliance is removed, the pubic area should be thoroughly washed, dried, and inspected for any soreness. If there is any soreness, the appliance should not be re-used until full healing has occurred.

Exercise 7.19

Catheters

A doctor will decide to use a urinary catheter when all other methods of managing incontinence are considered unsuitable. Catheters are only used to manage incontinence for those clients who need to be cared for in bed whilst being kept clean and dry and are unable to use a urinal, and for clients who have a continuous dribbling incontinence that is distressing the client.

Catheters are also used in hospitals for the following circumstances:

- To ensure that the bladder is empty prior to investigations or surgical procedures

- To facilitate drainage of urine and prevent/overcome retention of urine

- To ensure accurate measurement of urinary output for fluid balance purposes

The catheterisation of a client is usually only undertaken by a skilled practitioner. Catheters for short-term use are made of plastic or latex. Catheters for long-term use are usually coated with a substance, (e.g., silicone) so that they do not become encrusted with debris and become blocked. The catheter is kept in place by a small balloon on the catheter that is in-

flated inside the bladder. It is essential, therefore, that the client should not try to pull the catheter out whilst the balloon is inflated and that great care should be taken in moving these clients to ensure that tension is not placed on the catheter.

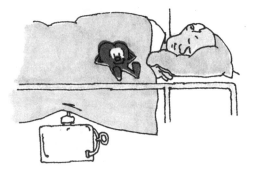

The correct length of catheter should be used; female catheters are shorter than male catheters. The carer needs to make sure that the catheter bag tubing is free from kinks and that the catheter bag is kept below the level of the bladder so that the urine can drain freely. Usually, during the day, a client will wear a urine bag holder which can hold a catheter bag in place on the leg.

A daily bath is usually provided so that the genitals and catheter can be kept clean. The catheter bag can be detached and a spigot (bung) placed in the end of the catheter. The catheter should be carefully washed with soap and water around the urethral opening.

Remember the following when an individual has a catheter:

- The catheter can be a source of urinary infection. The infected urine appears cloudy.

- The client should be encouraged to drink plenty of fluids (four pints per day).

- The catheter may become blocked or the drainage can be reduced if the client is constipated.

- A variety of catheter bags are available that can be worn (and hidden) under the clothes.

Exercise 7.20

Intermittent self-catheterisation is another option. Some health care professionals are not in favour of this controversial technique because it relies on social cleanliness, rather than aseptic technique.

Alternatively, a **suprapubic catheter** can be surgically inserted through the lower abdominal wall into the bladder as an alternative to the use of a long-term indwelling urinary catheter.

Management of Bowel Problems

The main treatment for **diarrhoea** is to treat the primary cause if there is one (e.g., antibiotics or food poisoning). In addition, the acute symptoms should be treated as follows:

- Taking no food by mouth except fluids until the diarrhoea settles down
- Ingesting a solution containing essential minerals (e.g., Dioralyte), if the diarrhoea is prolonged and/or if there has been vomiting
- Administering an anti-diarrhoeal treatment (e.g., diocalm tablets, kaolin and morphine mixture)
- Altering a client's diet (e.g., avoiding spicy food)
- Increasing the client's fluid intake to make up for what is being lost in the diarrhoea
- Providing soft or moistened toilet paper
- Ensuring easy access to toilet facilities
- Using a suitable barrier cream around the anus to prevent soreness

The main danger is that a person can become very dehydrated due to diarrhoea, especially if that individual is also vomiting. If dehydration starts to occur or if you feel that there is an underlying disease that needs treatment, the doctor should be summoned immediately.

Acute constipation can cause both bowel and urinary incontinence. For acute constipation the immediate aim is to evacuate the bowel as quickly and as completely as possible. To achieve this, laxatives, suppositories, and enemas are the preferred treatments. Once the bowel has been properly evacuated, conservative management of diet, fluids, and exercise can then be used to maintain normal bowel function.

The minimum treatment necessary should be used to clear the bowels. Laxatives should be used first. If they do not work, use a suppository. If that doesn't work, use an enema. Occasionally, an enema will be given straight away to relieve the discomfort of severe faecal impaction so that the laxative can then take effect.

Laxatives (purgatives, aperients) are taken orally. There are four different types:

- *Stool softeners* act by allowing the surface of faeces to absorb water which softens the stool (e.g., liquid paraffin). They usually take 24-48 hours to work.
- *Osmotic agents* exert an osmotic effect in the bowels, increasing the faecal weight, volume, and water content (e.g., magnesium sulphate, lactulose).
- *Stimulants* irritate the nerves in the gut wall to stimulate peristalsis in the small and large bowels (e.g., preparations containing danthron).
- *Bulking agents* work by retaining water in the faeces and microbial growth in the colon in order to increase faecal mass which stimulates peristalsis (e.g., fibrogel). They should be used in conjunction with an increased fluid intake. In most cases, though, introducing bran into the diet will achieve the same effects.

After a person has taken laxatives that have worked, there can be a period of no bowel evacuations. This may cause the person to think that they are again constipated, and lead them to taking more laxatives. Thus, a cycle of dependency occurs.

Suppositories promote evacuation of the bowel. The procedure for the administration of a suppository can be seen in Module 4, Part 4. The client is asked to retain the suppository for up to 20 minutes before attempting to empty the bowel. Suppositories are never given when there is chronic constipation that would require their repeated use.

Exercise 7.21 🖊

Enemas can be defined as the introduction of a stream of fluid into the rectum for the purpose of stimulating a bowel action or introducing medication. Enemas are never given when there is paralytic ileus, colonic obstruction, or when the introduction of fluids into the bowel may cause further health problems.

The procedure outlined here should be used for the giving of a disposable enema. Collect the following equipment—disposable incontinence pad, disposable gloves, swabs or tissues, lubricating jelly, enema pack. Then follow this procedure:

1. Allow the client to empty his or her bladder (also allow the client to empty his or her bowels if it is a medication enema).

2. Explain and discuss the procedure with the client, and ensure privacy.

3. Ensure that a bedpan, toilet, or commode is readily available.

4. Warm the enema to approximately 41°C (38°C for oil retention enemas) by placing it in a jug of warm water.

5. Assist the client to lie in the left lateral position (on the left side with the knees flexed and the buttocks near to the edge of the bed.

6. Place the disposable incontinence pad underneath the client's hips and buttocks.

7. Wash your hands with bacteriocidal soap and water or bacteriocidal alcohol hand rub, and put on the gloves.

8. Squeeze some lubricating jelly on a swab or tissue and lubricate the nozzle of the enema.

9. Expel any air from the enema nozzle just prior to separating the client's buttocks and slowly inserting the nozzle into the anal canal to a depth of no more than 10-12.5 cms so that the nozzle end is in the rectum.

10. Slowly introduce the enema fluid into the rectum by gently squeezing the enema container. The larger evacuant enema container can be slowly rolled up from the bottom to the top to prevent backflow. Ensure that all the enema contents are squeezed into the rectum.

11. Slowly withdraw the enema nozzle, and dry the client's anal area with a tissue or swab.

12. For an evacuant enema, ask the client to retain the contents of the enema for 10-15 minutes before evacuating the bowel. Ensure that the client has easy access to a call system and bedpan, toilet or commode, and toilet paper.

13. For a retention enema, elevate the foot of the bed, and leave the client for as long as prescribed.

14. Remove and dispose of all equipment, and wash your hands.

15. Record that the enema has been given and (for evacuant enemas) the results of the enema in terms of colour, consistency, content, and amount of faeces produced.

Exercise 7.22 🖊

Part 2: Enabling Movement and Achieving Comfort (Z7)

Enable others to be as independent in their movements as possible.

Manual handling procedures involve both hazards and risks. A hazard can be defined as something which may cause harm. Risk is an expression of the probability of harm or injury occurring. Hazards and risks are present for both carers and clients involved in manual handling.

The stresses exerted on the spine during manual handling tasks are mainly the result of the techniques used. The Manual Handling Operations Regulations provide clear guidelines on moving and lifting practice and a framework for risk assessment. You must use only those lifting and moving techniques that are sanctioned by your employing organisation.

Exercise 7.23 🖉

Information concerning the lifting and moving of clients and the relationship to personal health and safety can be found in Module 3, Part 2. Refer to the table below when deciding on whether a lift is safe or not.

	Lifting Capacities		
	1 Carer	2 Carers	3 Carers
Men	25 kg (3 st 13 lb)	33.3 kg (5 st 13 lb)	37.5 kg (5 st 12 lb)
Women	16.6 kg (2 st 8 lb)	22.2 kg (3 st 7 lb)	25 kg (3 st 13 lb)

The weight capacities outlined above are only for lifting in the ideal position with the load being held close to the lower body of all the carers.

Exercise 7.24 🖉

The emphasis, therefore, is placed on avoiding manual lifting, whenever possible. In the ideal situation, when clients require assistance with mobility, there should be hoists, sliding aids, and handling slings available. An employer who does not make this kind of equipment and associated training available is in conflict with the law. So are the carers who choose to ignore the equipment and systems of safe practice that are implemented locally for their own safety and protection.

You are required to adapt the task to suit the environment, the available manual handling aids, and the skills and physical abilities of the individuals undertaking the task. The expectation is that all lifting and moving tasks must be assessed *in advance* every time the task has to be carried out. Where possible, involve the client in the decision making on the level of support that is needed for the move.

The emphasis is placed on taking action to remove or reduce the risk of injury to all participants. The actions and support provided, therefore, should be consistent with the plan of care and the outcomes of the initial assessment. It is essential for you to recognise that when a manual handling task is beyond your capabilities, you need to be assertive enough to refuse to undertake the task until additional equipment and/or assistance is available. You should then report the situation to an appropriate member of the care team. Help may be available from a number of sources (e.g., the ambulance service in the community).

Many clients are able to assist the carers who are moving them. They should be encouraged to do so, as long as it is in ways that are appropriate to their capabilities and health status.

Exercise 7.25 🖉

Moving and Handling Guidelines

The lifting or moving task that needs to be achieved should be clearly defined. If necessary, the task should be divided into sub-tasks that can be assessed separately (e.g., from lying on the bed to being sat at the edge of the bed to transfer to a chair).

Check the client's care plan, and assess the needs of the client and any limitations imposed by the care environment or available resources, using the flow diagram below, and inform all care staff involved in the task. If you are unsure about how to undertake the manual handling task or if you are not sure whether the proposed move or transfer is safe, this should be reported to the person-in-charge. If available, contact your organisation's manual handling coordinator for advice.

With the client's permission, prepare the care area by moving all unnecessary furniture and equipment out of the way. Inform the client what you are about to do, even when the client is unconscious. Your aims are to move the client in ways which minimise pain, discomfort, and friction whilst maximising independence, self-respect, and dignity.

A flowchart for providing guidance on the moving and handling of clients, can be seen below.

Flowchart for the Manual Handling of Clients

Exercise 7.26 🖉

Assemble the appropriate manual handling equipment and personnel, and help the client into the desired position. Ensure that the client is comfortable before you return the client's furniture and equipment to their usual places.

Safely store away the manual handling equipment. Record in the client's care record when you find a method of moving/handling that is acceptable to all. Also, record any problems in manual handling, and changes in the client's health or abilities.

Exercise 7.27 🖉

Remember the following rules:

· Always use manual handling aids, when they are available and appropriate for the task in hand. Make sure that they are in good working order.

· The task must be designed so that it avoids stooping and/or twisting with a load.

· Pushing and pulling are preferred to lifting a load. Even these activities are not totally risk-free.

· Take into account the possibility that the load might move suddenly (e.g., client becomes aggressive or faints).

· People do not have handles. Therefore, use handling aids, rather than grasping a client under the arm pits.

· Beware of space constraints. Although some furniture can be moved out of the way, narrow toilets, wheelchairs, etc., always make manual handling more difficult. If unsure, use a hoist.

· Make sure you are dressed appropriately for manual handling (e.g., loose fitting clothing and flat-heeled shoes).

· Adaptations to planned moves may need to be used if activities in addition to manual handling have to be undertaken at the same time (e.g., inserting a bedpan, adjusting clothing, guarding clinical equipment such as catheters, intravenous infusions).

- The usual way to coordinate a lift is to say "1-2-3, lift." Unfortunately, some carers commence the lift on "3" and some on "lift." It has been suggested the words, "Ready, brace, push/slide/pull/stand" should be used.

- Remember to evaluate each manual handling operation. If any changes or adaptations are required, make sure that these are well documented.

- If a client appears to be falling at any time, do not try to catch him or her; simply support the person so that he or she falls in a controlled fashion to the floor, bed, or chair, minimising the risk of injuries to all concerned.

- If you find a client on the floor, make him or her as comfortable as possible. Do not attempt to move the person until properly assessed for injuries. Always use a hoist to get a client up from the floor, unless the person can get up without help, or unless the position puts the person in further danger.

- Do not utilise personnel for manual handling unless they have been appropriately trained for the moves and equipment that are to be used, and you are sure that they are physically fit enough for the task.

- If a safe manual handling solution cannot be found, the client should remain in bed until appropriate equipment can be obtained.

- If the client's preferences conflict with safe practice, inform the person-in-charge.

- Any long-term environmental constraints to manual handling (e.g., steps, uneven floor, narrow doorway) should be reported so that the environment can be speedily adapted for the needs of the client(s).

Exercise 7.28 🖉

The experience of being moved physically by others can be unpleasant and frightening, especially if no prior explanation or warning has been given by the carers to the client.

Lifting and Moving Aids

Remember that the aims of utilising manual handling equipment include the following:

- Help clients to achieve more independence.
- Provide a safe way of moving or transferring a client from one place to another.
- Achieve physical comfort whilst maintaining the dignity of clients.
- Minimise the potential hazards of manual handling.

Manual handling aids improve the carer's manual handling technique, while allowing the client more independence.

Hoists can be attached to an overhead track or hung from a mobile stand. The most popular is the hand or battery-operated mobile hoist that enables a non-weight-bearing individual to be transferred from one area to another. The hoists can usually be adapted for a number of lifting tasks, including the use of fixed chairs and slings.

A **transfer belt** fits around a client's waist and has handles. This enables the carer to push, pull, assist, or guide a client without having to bend into a dangerous position or put his or her arms around the client. The belt is usually adjustable so that it can fit a variety of people, and it often includes looped handholds. The belt should not be used for lifting clients. Narrow belts that are unpadded can dig into a client's waist.

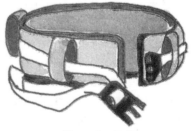

Transfer Belt

183

Sliding Board

A **sliding board** can be a one-piece transfer board which has one low friction surface and a non-smooth surface that will not slip. Alternatively, it can be a board that has a sliding section where the friction occurs between the board and the sliding section. A sliding board is simply used to bridge a gap (e.g., between wheelchair and bed) so that the client can slide him/herself along the board. The boards come in different sizes, widths, lengths, and curves. They are cheap and portable. The transfer is usually easier if the two surfaces are level and the client has good sitting balance.

A **supine transfer board** is usually a large, solid board that has one slippery surface to allow the transfer of a supine (laid on back) patient from one level surface to another (e.g., from trolley to bed). It can be used in conjunction with a sliding sheet. The board can be easily stored, and some versions have handholds or handles built in to the device.

Sliding sheets are available in many forms, including cushioned varieties. They are useful for clients who have difficulty in moving or positioning themselves in bed or who can be safely transferred onto a level surface without the aid of a hoist. Instead of manually lifting the client, he or she is pulled or slid up or across the bed by one or two carers. Most sliding sheets are tubular in design, with a slippery nylon inner surface and a non-slip outer surface. Some versions have handholds sewn into the fabric that can be grasped by carers.

For clients who tend to slide down the bed (in conjunction with a slightly tilted bed), the client can be left on a one-way slide sheet, which slides easily in one direction and prevents sliding in the opposite direction. The sheets are especially useful for sliding under clients who have fallen into tight spaces like a toilet floor and need to be moved to where a hoist can be used. Preferably, all clients should have their own sliding sheets.

A **bed ladder** is a ladder with solid rungs and rope sides which is usually attached to the foot of a bed. It is an inexpensive device that allows a client who has good arm strength, to grab hold of the lower rungs and gradually climb up the ladder using the hands, until a sitting position is reached.

A **monkey pole** is a swinging bar hanging over the bed from a metal frame. The client grasps the bar with both hands to lift his bottom clear of the bed to relieve pressure, to move up or turn in bed, to enable a carer to insert a sliding sheet, and/or to strengthen the arm muscles. It cannot be used to help a client move up the bed.

Monkey Pole

Turning discs are usually made of two discs that rotate against each other. There are two main types— the moulded plastic and the flexible fabric. It can be used, for example, by a person who has just transferred from a wheelchair to a car seat. The device enables the person to swing his or her feet inside the car.

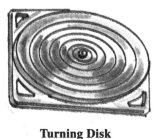

Turning Disk

Handling slings are positioned under the client's thighs, buttocks, or hips, so that the carer does not have to lean too far forward to achieve a good grip (e.g., when sliding a client up the bed).

Hand blocks are provided for clients who can support their upper bodies, lean forward a little, and have good hand and arm strength. They are placed at either side of a client who is sat in bed to lift his or her bottom clear of the bed, relieve pressure on the bottom, or for the person to move/slide up the bed.

Exercise 7.29 🖉

One of the great challenges for carers is to undertake the manual handling of a confused and/or frightened client. The aim is to allow the client to feel calm and safe and willing to cooperate and/or help. You should utilise a confident tone of voice and a smile. If necessary, leave the client alone for a while to calm down.

There are at least 60 different types of hoists and 150 lifting and moving aids available for care settings. Not all care environments provide the carers with the lifting aids that they need, nor the training to use them. As carers utilise the lifting and moving aids, they become more proficient in their use. Remember, though, that, even when hoists are being used, there is usually still the need to pull and push the hoist around.

Beds

In relation to caring for clients on beds, ask yourself these questions. **First, is the client on the correct type of bed?** In their own homes, clients are cared for on their own beds. In care facilities, most clients are still provided with King's Fund beds. These beds are now considered as being suitable only for clients who have few mobility problems. (This applies to few patients admitted to hospitals nowadays.)

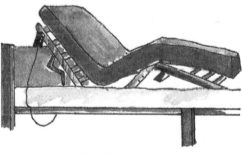

Profiling Bed

The best option is a four-section profiling bed. The bed enables a client to be sat up or laid down in bed without any need for manual handling. In addition, the client can move, without having to call for help from a carer. Heavy duty and specialist beds are available for very large clients and clients who have specialist health problems (e.g., quadriplegia).

Second, is the client on the correct type of mattress? All clients who are at risk from developing pressure sores should be cared for on one of the types of mattress that reduce pressure to the 'at-risk' areas of the body. The investment in a pressure-relieving mattress more than outweighs the costs of the extra care needed for someone who develops a pressure sore and the misery and discomfort the pressure sore causes for the client.

Third, does the bed allow the use of the manual handling devises that are needed for this client? One problem that can occur here is when the base of the bed prevents the use of a mobile hoist.

Exercise 7.30 🖉

Common Manual Handling Situations

Turning the client in bed is usually referred to as *log rolling*. The manoeuvre is used for a number of reasons—changing bed linen, inserting hoist slings and slide sheets, turning a client in bed in order to prevent pressure sores, and to aid the drainage of secretions from the lungs. A client will be turned a full 90 degrees for the changing of sheets, but may only be turned/tilted approximately 30 degrees (less than a full turn) for the purpose of trying to relieve the pressure areas.

Turning a Client in Bed

The best way to turn a client in bed is to use a cushioned sliding sheet which can be left in place, in readiness for the next log roll. These are sheets designed to slide from side to side and allow a client to be turned in bed using minimum effort. Follow this procedure:

1. Lower or higher the bed to the carer's waist level.

2. Position the sliding sheet under the client with the open ends of the sheet facing the top and bottom of the bed.

3. Turn the client's head to face the direction of the move.

4. The arm on the side of the body on which the client is to be rolled, should be bent at the elbow and placed so that it does not end up under the body after the roll.

5. The other arm should be placed across the client's chest.

6. The leg which will be on top when the client has been rolled onto his or her side, should be slightly bent and pulled forward.

7. The carer can then roll the client towards him or her, using the shoulder and knee as levers; OR, pull on the sliding sheet to roll the client, ensuring that there is someone on the opposite side of the bed or that a padded bed side is left up so that the client cannot fall out of bed. Do not forget to lower the bed side once the procedure has been completed.

8. Maintain the client's position by the use of pillows behind the client's back, and/or between the legs, and/or against the chest.

9. Ensure that there are no creases that might damage the client's skin.

Heavier clients will require two or more carers for the log roll. Additional carers may also be required if the client is uncooperative or is attached to medical equipment (e.g., urinary catheter, intravenous infusion).

Exercise 7.31

Sitting a client forward in bed is often done by asking the client to bend forward from a supine position. A profiling bed will sit a client up for you automatically. Where possible, always allow a client to sit him/herself up (e.g., using a bed ladder).

Sitting forward can be very difficult for clients who are frail, confused, unwell, or who have abdominal injuries or wounds. The upper part of the body can be very heavy; you should estimate that, in a paralysed or uncooperative client, you may be exposed to lifting up to a third of the client's body weight. This is obviously unacceptable, so the following techniques are provided only for clients who can help when they are being sat forward in bed.

Follow this procedure only with cooperative clients:

1. The bed is adjusted to a fairly low position.

2. The carers on either side of the bed face the client, and each places the inside knee and foot on the bed, at the level of the client's hip.

3. Each carer uses an elbow-to-elbow grip with the client's arms.

4. The outside arm of each carer is then free (e.g., to plump up the client's pillows).

An alternate procedure follows:

1. Place a draw sheet or folded sheet between the client and the bed, stretching from hip to shoulder.

Sitting Client Forward

2. The carers kneel on the bed as in the other procedure, and the sheet can then be grasped by the carers. The client can be pulled towards them using the sheet instead of the elbow-to-elbow grip.

Exercise 7.32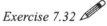

Moving a Seated Client Up or Down the Bed

When cared for in a profiling bed, a client should not need to be moved up or down the bed. If the client has slipped down the bed, the bed can be adjusted into a semi-chair shape, and the client automatically slides back down into position.

If a client can help in moving him/herself up the bed, rock the client from side to side onto a fabric slide. The client can then be encouraged to slide up the bed by pushing with the legs and/or by the use of bed blocks. When necessary, help can be provided by the carer. The client bends his or her legs and the carer holds the feet in place; when the client straightens the legs, he or she moves up the bed.

The method outlined below is for clients who can sit up in bed. It should not be used for people who cannot sit up unsupported; who are confused; who have injuries to their shoulders, chests or backs; or who have little or no control over their heads and necks.

1. Set the height of the bed at waist level. When there are two people of different heights, the knee height of the shorter one dictates the height of the bed.

2. The sliding sheet is positioned underneath the client using a log rolling technique. The open ends of the sheet should be facing the sides of the bed.

3. Then re-set the height of the bed at just above knee level.

4. The client is helped into a sitting position with both carers facing the opposite way to the client.

5. The inside knee and foot of the carer is placed on the bed, next to the client, at the level of the person's buttocks. The outside foot remains on the floor, close to the bed and parallel to the inside knee. The knee of the outside leg is slightly bent.

6. The carer's inside hand takes hold of the handling sling, whilst the outside hand

187

gently grasps the client's hand to provide balance and support.

7. One of the carers takes the lead in commencing the move (e.g., saying "Ready, brace, slide"). The two carers then sit back onto their heels whilst holding onto the slide, moving the client into the required position.

8. If the client has not moved up the bed enough, the carers reposition themselves and repeat the move.

Moving On/Off the Bed in a Supine Position

This move is often used for unconscious clients, and it most commonly occurs between the bed and a trolley, and between a trolley and an operating table. There is no safe way to lift a supine client from one flat surface to another. Even poles and canvas are now thought to be unsafe for the transfer.

The easiest and safest way is to use a hard or soft sliding device. Devices are all used in a similar fashion.

1. Half roll the client away from the direction of travel using a log rolling technique (see above), and insert the slide.

2. Then roll the client back onto the slide.

3. Push or pull the client across to the other surface, and remove the slide. (Usually a slide can be removed without having to roll the client again.)

Exercise 7.33 🖊

Changing bed linen, with a client in bed, is only carried out when a client is on full bed rest and is not allowed to get out of bed. The basic method is to adapt the log rolling technique:

1. The client is rolled onto his or her side, and the soiled bed linen is tightly rolled up behind the client. If necessary the bed and mattress can be cleaned, disinfected, and dried at this point. The client can also be cleansed and have the pressure areas checked.

2. A clean sheet is then placed where the soiled bed linen has been removed, and the excess is rolled up tightly behind the client next to the soiled linen. If necessary, an incontinence pad can be used to create a barrier between the clean and soiled linen to prevent the clean linen from becoming soiled.

3. The client can then be rolled back over both sets of bed linen and onto his or her other side.

4. The soiled bed linen is now removed and disposed of, and the clean sheet can be pulled out so that it can be spread over the whole mattress. If necessary, the client's soiled clothing can be removed and replaced.

5. Ensure that the client is exposed as little as possible during the procedure to prevent chilling and minimise embarrassment.

When **standing a client up**, follow these precautions:

- Do not lift a client manually to a standing position.

- Take extra care if a client has previously fallen. Do not allow yourself to be used as a prop.

- Do not encourage a client to move to a standing position unless you are reasonably sure the person can take his or her own weight and that this can be achieved with minimal support and assistance.

- When a client is to stand from a sitting position, make sure the person is in an appropriate chair (e.g., the chair should not be too soft, too low, or too deep).

- Check whether the client uses a walking stick or walking frame for balance and support.

- Ensure there is enough room for the client and for you to provide support.

- Ensure the client's clothing and shoes are appropriate for the task.

- Provide as little support as needed, so that the client can be as independent as possible.

Procedure for standing up a client:

1. If the client needs support whilst standing, ensure that he or she wears a handling belt.

2. Ask the client to shuffle the hips forward so that he or she is sat forward on the seat.

3. Ask the client to lean forward, with the nose over the toes.

4. Ensure that the feet are positioned so that one knee is at a right angle with the foot flat on the floor, and the other foot is positioned to the side slightly behind the first foot.

5. If necessary, rock the client back and forwards a couple of times, prior to standing, in order to gain the momentum necessary to stand.

6. Ask the client to straighten the legs whilst using the arms of the chair for support, and then encourage the client to stand erect and look straight ahead.

7. On standing, once the person feels balanced, he or she can then grasp the walking stick or walking frame before moving away.

8. Make sure that there are enough carers present to provide the support that the client needs. If, at any point, the person appears to be losing balance or starts to fall, do not try to catch the person, just lower him or her as gently as possible back into the chair.

Exercise 7.34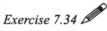

When **helping a client to walk**, the care worker is usually positioned at the side of the client. Although you are providing support at waist height, the load must be taken on one side (leading to the spine being unbalanced).

If a client starts to fall or faint, you will have to twist to provide support, and this is very dangerous. You should release the client's hand, and move behind the client. Take one step back so that you can provide some support as the client slides to the floor.

Follow these precautions to avoid falls:

- If you are not well matched with the client in terms of height, be especially careful.

- Preferably, the client should wear a handling belt.

- If there is only one carer available, the carer should stand on the client's weak side, holding the client's right hand in his or her right hand (or vice versa). The client's arm should be straight so that the client can press down on the carer's palm with his or her palm (thumbs interlocking) to gain support.

- Where necessary, the client can be followed around by another carer pushing a wheelchair, in case the client becomes tired and needs to sit down quickly.

Toileting

In bed: The insertion of a bedpan is easy if the supine client can bridge (raise the buttocks off the bed). A monkey pole can be useful here. The bedpan is simply slipped under the client without any need for manual handling. If not, then the client is rolled onto his or her side. The bedpan is put in position, and the client is rolled onto it. If the client is very heavy, a hoist needs to be used.

Where feasible, the client can then be sat up on the bedpan. It is not uncommon for a person to be unsteady or feel unsafe whilst perched on the bedpan. If necessary, the carer can support the client when using the bedpan, but most clients will prefer privacy. Therefore, when possible, it is better to ensure that the client has bed sides or hand blocks for support. If a client simply wants to pass urine, it is usually better to use a male or female urinal, as appropriate.

Sometimes a heavy, community-based client can suddenly become dependent and unable to move him/herself. Until a full assessment can be undertaken and a hoist provided, it may be necessary to temporarily catheterise the client.

At the toilet: When a client cannot be safely transferred to the toilet inside a narrow toilet cubicle, it is appropriate to transfer the client to a mobile *sanichair* outside the cubicle where there is more room. The client can then be pushed over the toilet whilst sat on the sanichair. In this case the external door to the toilet area will need to be locked so that the client can have privacy.

A sanichair should have castors and a braking mechanism on all four legs. It should also have foot rests which can be moved to one side when a client is trying to get on or off the sanichair.

An individual carer should not be expected to carry out other tasks whilst supporting a client who is getting up or sitting down on a toilet or sanichair. If the client needs wiping, or if clothes need to be adjusted, this should be done by another carer.

If a client finds mobilisation difficult, it is best to avoid the stress of attempting to get to the toilet in time, as this may lead to a fall. Take the client to the toilet on a wheelchair, and let him or her walk back.

Exercise 7.35 🖉

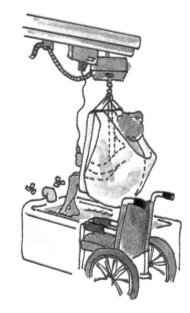

Washing and Bathing

Washing and bathing clients can be hard work for carers. There are a number of ways that a dependent client can maintain personal hygiene:

- Having a strip wash
- Being given a bed bath
- Having a bath, if appropriate bathing aids are available
- Having a shower whilst seated

These choices should enable you to help a client meet personal hygiene needs whilst maintaining privacy and comfort.

For washing and bathing clients, ensure that carers have a comfortable working posture. Allow the client to be as independent as possible, within the bounds of safety. Do not, under any circumstances, lift a client in or out of the bath. Allow clients who can use a bath to enter from a sitting position; stepping over the bath side increases the risk of the client slipping or losing balance. Whenever possible, use non-slip bath aids for the client to sit/stand on.

Clients Who Have Collapsed on the Floor

Whether a client has just collapsed or you have simply found a client on the floor, you should first assess the client to see if he or she has suffered a respiratory or cardiac arrest. Then check for injuries, and try and find out why the person has collapsed.

Leave the client where he or she is, as long as there is no danger, until the person has received treatment or regains consciousness. Following are the only reasons you would attempt to move the client immediately:

- You are in water, and the client may drown.

- There is danger from a fire, smoke, or fumes.

- There is an obvious physical danger (e.g., from a bomb, a bullet, an aggressive person, falling masonry).

Never try to manually lift a client from the floor. There is a very great risk of injury to the carers. If the client cannot get him/herself up from the floor, use a hoist to move the person. If necessary, slide the person out of a tight space on a sliding sheet first.

Occasionally you will encounter a client who throws him/herself out of bed or injures oneself against the bed frame. You can provide one-to-one care to prevent the client from injuring him/herself. If the human resources are not available, you will have to care for the client on (a mattress on) the floor. The client will then have to be lifted by hoist onto a bed every time you want to provide care. You must not try

to provide care at floor level because this will mean using a "risky" posture.

Exercise 7.36 🖉

Getting In and Out of a Car

Clients who can stand present few problems when getting in and out of a car. The wheelchair is positioned close to the car so that the person can either slide across, or stand up and lower him/herself into the car seat, then swivel to get feet and legs into the car.

When transferring a person with mobility problems into a car, note that a two-door car usually has more space for the transfer than a four-door car. Never try to transfer a person into the rear seat of a two-door car.

Use the following procedure:

1. The car should be parked so that the car seat and the wheelchair are on the same level.

2. The footplates of the wheelchair are pushed back, and the person's feet are placed on the edge of the door frame. The person's bottom should be at the same level as the back of the car seat.

3. The inside armrest of the wheelchair is removed to allow the transfer across to the car seat.

4. If the person leans away from the car, a transfer board can be placed under the person to span the gap between the wheelchair and the car seat.

5. The person then leans slightly forward and slides or shuffles across onto the car seat. The legs should follow and fall into place in front of the car seat.

6. When required, a soft turning disc or a plastic carrier bag can be used to help the person turn once he or she has sat in the car seat.

Exercise 7.37 🖉

Providing Pressure Area Care

The skin is the body's largest organ. It is easily damaged. The skin of people who are ill and/or who are old, is especially vulnerable. Preventing problems is a lot easier than healing damaged skin. Clients most at risk include those who:

- Are immobile and inactive
- Are incontinent
- Are unconscious
- Are over or underweight
- Have an infection or circulatory disease
- Have poor personal hygiene

Lying or sitting in one position for too long causes pressure over bony prominences. Pressure affects the blood supply to the skin and underlying tissues. If an area of skin does not receive an adequate blood supply, it becomes damaged and may die.

Exercise 7.38 🖊

Pressure Sores

The terms **pressure sore or decubitus ulcer** are used to describe an area of damage to the skin or underlying tissue caused by direct pressure or shearing forces. Pressure sores tend to occur over the body's bony prominences (noted in the illustration below).

Pressure sores develop in four stages:

1. A pink or red area on the skin does not disappear within 15 minutes after the pressure has been relieved.

2. The skin is cracked, blistered, or broken, and the surrounding area is red.

3. The skin breaks down, and the subcutaneous tissue is exposed.

4. The sore penetrates to the muscle or bone, and there may be infection and drainage of fluid.

Exercise 7.39 🖊

To prevent pressure sores, follow these **general guidelines**:

Relieve Pressure: Rotate an immobile client's position every two hours. Use appropriate pressure-relieving devises to redistribute the pressure and support pillows to maintain position.

Prevent Friction and Shearing: Never rub the skin vigorously (including rubbing with soap and water and/or oil). Avoid dragging a person in bed as this can shear the skin, and avoid wrinkles in sheets and clothing on which a person is sat or laid.

Control Moisture: Keep clients clean and dry (especially if they are incontinent or perspiring a lot).

Prevent Skin Trauma: Keep your nails short so that you do not accidentally scratch others. Do not wear jewelry or badges that could damage a client's skin.

Exercise 7.40 🖊

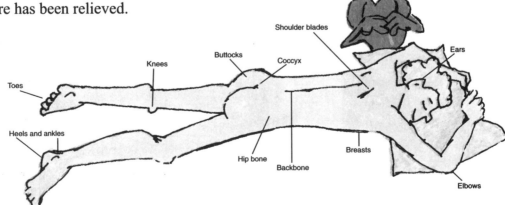

Make sure that all of the clients in your care have been assessed using a recognised pressure area assessment tool (e.g., Norton or Waterlow), that has been ratified by your employing organisation. When there is a change in a client's condition, the client should be reassessed.

Do not rub any areas at risk of developing pressure sores as this may cause damage or degeneration of the skin. Wash only the areas of the body at risk, if the client has been incontinent, or if he or she has been sweating profusely. Ensure that all the soap is rinsed off and that the area is patted, rather than rubbed, dry.

If the skin is dry, use moisturiser. Ask the client about his or her preferences. Only use a barrier cream when needed.

Educate and encourage the client to regularly change his or her own position. Provide help, when needed. This can be incorporated into a physiotherapy, occupational therapy, and/or mobility programme, and other activities of daily living. If the client cannot regularly examine his or her own pressure areas, you must do it for the client.

Relieve the pressure over those parts of the body that are vulnerable to breaking down into pressure sores. When available, use one or more pressure relief devises. If necessary, turn the client at least two-hourly, recording the client's position on the relevant chart, each time the client has been turned.

Encourage clients to sit up in chairs or in their beds, if they are able. Where possible, use a bean bag to help with positioning in bed, rather than the bed's backrest. Don't forget that the periods of time that a client can be left sat up in a chair may need to be reduced if sacral or pelvic sores start to develop.

Where possible, clients should be involved in their own care planning to minimise the effects of pressure. Remember to use a level and pace of discussion that is appropriate for each client. Inform them about the factors that cause pressure sores, and encourage the clients to be as active as possible and to do as much

as they can for themselves, resulting in the pressure being naturally relieved.

Also, remember that you are caring for the whole client, not just the pressure areas. Encourage the client to be assertive in providing ongoing feedback on the level of comfort or discomfort that he or she is experiencing. Take the client's preferences into account when providing care.

Therefore, whilst positioning and supporting the client in a manner that minimises pressure, you will also need to ensure that other needs are taken into consideration.

- **Dress** the client so that the client's mode of dress is as "normal" as possible (e.g., unless the client is ill, it would be inappropriate to be dressed in pyjamas all the time). Ensure that clothing does not inhibit pressure area care (e.g., by being too tight) and that it does does not cause pressure sores (e.g., from creases, buttons, zips, and seams)

- **Position** the client so that the client can see as much of the environment as possible and so that he or she can engage in social activities (e.g., converse with other clients, participate in a game of draughts). The position should allow the person to be as self-caring as possible (e.g., feeding, personal hygiene).

Ensure that the plan of care relating to pressure areas is carried out as specified. If you encounter any problems in carrying out the plan of care (e.g., the client's condition changes or other care needs require the care for pressure areas to be changed), immediately report this to the person-in-charge.

Exercise 7.41 🖊

Clients who are at a high risk of developing pressure sores should be checked more often (e.g., every time their positions are changed). You need to have an awareness of normal skin colours for different racial groups, before you can detect the changes that occur due to a developing pressure sore.

Pressure-Relieving Equipment

Because some clients cannot change their positions on a regular basis, a variety of devises have been produced for relieving pressure to specific areas of the body. These can be used to prevent a pressure sore from developing or to relieve pressure once a pressure sore has developed. Pressure-relieving equipment should be used, cleaned, maintained, and stored in accordance with the manufacturer's instructions.

The choice of pressure-relieving devise must be specific to meet a client's individual need.

- A **sheepskin** is warm and comfortable under the body. It is particularly good at protecting heels, although it does not relieve the pressure. A sheepskin will tend to harden and matt after it has been washed several times. It needs changing frequently and is not appropriate for clients who are regularly incontinent.

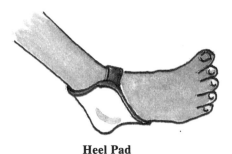

Heel Pad

- **Heel and elbow pads** can be made of sheepskin, foam, or silicone. They reduce friction and shearing forces to elbows and heels. They can sometimes be difficult to keep in place, and they harden with repeated washing.
- **Pressure-relieving mattresses** include low air loss mattress, alternating pressure mattress, bead mattress, and fibre-filled overlay mattress. One commonly used type of mattress is the alternating pressure mattress

which can be made to fit any bed. It reduces the frequency (but not the need for) regular turning. Despite being prone to breakdown, the mattress is comfortable and can be wiped down and disinfected when used for incontinent clients.

- **Special beds** are used when the client is too ill to be moved very much (e.g., spinal injury units). Here, for example, a rocker bed can be used so that the bed can be tilted to shift the client's position, rather than the client having to be moved on the bed.

Exercise 7.42 ✐

The **treatment of pressure sores** is the same as for any other wound. Care should be focused on relieving the cause (e.g., pressure, shearing forces) and minimising the symptoms from any underlying health problems. Guidelines for the provision of dressings, which are needed when a pressure sore has resulted in the skin being broken, can be seen in Module 4, Part 2.

Summary

People in your care depend on you to help them achieve whatever level of comfort is possible. One major area of concern is enabling people to meet their elimination needs. Understanding basic anatomy and physiology is important for recognizing and treating specific incontinence problems.

Another major area of concern is moving and positioning clients. Never undertake any manual handling procedures or equipment unless you have been properly trained. It is very important to use manual handling techniques that are safe and prevent harm (for both the clients and those providing care).

Check Your Knowledge and Understanding

1. A rather large client has asked to be moved up the bed. An experienced member of care staff who comes over to help you states that she does not like all these "new fangled" sliding sheets and devises and refuses to use them. She suggests that you use the Australian (shoulder) lift to move the client up the bed. What would you do?

   a) Go ahead and use the Australian lift because there is nobody else available to help you at the moment.

   b) Insist that the other member of staff helps you to use a slide sheet to move the client up the bed.

   c) Slide the person up the bed by yourself.

   d) Gently explain that you would prefer to use the equipment that has been provided for this purpose as it is safer for everyone concerned and, therefore, you will wait until someone else is available to help you.

2. You are talking to a teenage girl who says that she never has her bowels open more than once a week. What would you do?

   a) Advise the girl to start increasing the amount of roughage in her diet.

   b) Accept that the frequency of this girl's bowel actions is normal for her, unless she states that there is a problem.

   c) Ensure that a full continence assessment is carried out at the earliest opportunity.

   d) Assess the girl's dietary intake to see if that is the cause of her problem.

3. A client complains that she needs to go to the toilet to pass urine up to twice per hour and that sometimes she is wet by the time she gets to the toilet. What would you do?

   a) Advise the woman to drink at least three litres of fluid per day and to obtain some "potassium citrate" from the chemist, which should be taken as per the pharmacist's instructions until she can get an appointment to see the doctor.

   b) Ensure that a full continence assessment is carried out at the earliest opportunity.

   c) Recommend that the woman should reduce her intake of coffee and tea to a minimum.

   d) Request the general practitioner to refer the woman to a genito-urinary specialist at the hospital.

4. A man has been admitted to your care facility after having a minor stroke. He cannot walk and has to be propped up in bed, and he needs help with all his self-care needs. He says he would like to have a bath, and he insists that the hoist is not used to get him into and out of the bath. What would you do?

   a) Insist that if the man wants to have a bath, the hoist must be used. Alternatively, offer him a bed bath.

   b) Offer the man the chance to use the shower instead.

   c) Agree to take the man to the bathroom in his wheelchair, and then slide him into and out of the bath from the wheelchair.

   d) Offer the man the chance to have a strip wash in the communal washroom.

5. An elderly man has been admitted to your care environment for stabilisation of his diabetes. He recently had an operation on his prostate gland, and now he appears to have a slight dribble incontinence. His clothing is wet, and he smells strongly of urine. What would you do?

a) Request the doctor to catheterise the man until he can be fully assessed.

b) Insist that the man wear a condom urinal until he is discharged.

c) Commence a continence assessment on the man, and arrange for him to be seen by the continence advisor at the earliest opportunity.

d) Ensure that the man has several changes of clothing, and that he is taken to the toilet hourly.

6. One of your clients has developed a chest infection. Usually he is quite healthy and fully mobile. But, at the moment, he has spent the last two days in bed. He has complained that his bottom is getting sore. When you inspect the area, you notice a small red area of skin around the sacrum. What would you do?

a) Immediately place the client on an alternating pressure mattress, and commence two-hourly turning.

b) Place a sheepskin mattress cover under the man, wash and dry the sacral area thoroughly, and ask him to keep turning himself so that he doesn't develop a pressure sore.

c) Undertake a Waterlow pressure area assessment, and then prepare a plan of care to overcome this problem.

d) Ask the man to lay on his side, rather than remain sat up in bed.

Answer Key

MODULE 1

Question 1   Answer: **b**

Explanation: It should not be your decision to break the rules of confidentiality in this case. The person-in-charge will probably decide to inform the child protection officer. He or she might also want to interview the parent first and inform the parent of the intentions.

Question 2   Answer: **c**

Explanation: It is best to let the nurse in charge deal with this request. A patient can compel the release of computerised medical records, unless it can be contested that sight of the records could be harmful to the patient. But, most hospitals have policies to deal with this situation. Policies can include the expectation that at least two days' notice is needed before a copy of medical records is provided, and there may be a charge levied for the service.

Question 3   Answer: **d**

Explanation: You have tried to politely stop this man from harassing you. It has not worked. Therefore, it is time to take this problem further and get it sorted out.

Question 4   Answers: **a and b**

Explanation: The needs of the person contemplating suicide and the needs of the abused child override the need to maintain confidentiality.

Question 5   Answer: **c**

Explanation: This is the only logical alternative that will meet this man's needs to fast and your need to ensure that he consumes a good diet in order to regain some of the weight that he has lost.

Question 6   Answer: **b**

Explanation: A reprimand is likely to escalate, rather than de-escalate the situation.

Question 7   Answer: **a**

Explanation: A clear, concise, and accurate objective report should be immediately written while the incident is still fresh in the memory.

Question 8   Answer: **c**

Explanation: If the person is only at slight risk from abuse, it is a waste of staff time to maintain constant supervision (especially if the person could be at risk for the rest of his life).

MODULE 2

Question 1   Answers: **all**

Explanation: They are all communication problems.

Question 2   Answer: **d**

Explanation: The only thing that matters is that when the lady is discharged, she takes her medication as prescribed and attends the day centre. Answer "d" is most likely to get that result.

Question 3   Answer: **a**

Explanation: If you ask the young man not to talk about the subject "b" or direct him to talk about something different "c," you are being directive and not client centred. If you try to cope with these strong feelings during the counselling session "d," there is likely to be congruence problems which may impinge on the relationship. Therefore, if you cannot offer the pre-requisites of non-directive, client-centred counselling, you must hand the client over to another counsellor "a" who can offer these pre-requisites.

Question 4   Answers: **b and c**

Explanation: Answer "b" is incorrect because nobody should be forced to use any language they do not feel comfortable using. Answer "c" is wrong because pressure should not be put on a person to talk about his problems when he is not yet ready to talk about them.

Question 5   Answer: **d**

Explanation: Reprimanding residents "a" is not the best way to form a therapeutic relationship. Ignoring the behaviour "b" is simply avoiding the problem. Moving him to a side ward and reminding carers not to bend down near him "c" is a way of managing the problem, but does not work on the source of the problem. In "d" this approach allows you to prevent the problem from happening whilst forming a positive relationship with this person and preventing him from having to be "isolated."

Question 6   Answer: **b**

Explanation: Relaxation techniques are easy to learn and would allow the friend to get on with his life.

MODULE 3

Question 1   Answer: **c**

Explanation: You need to conduct a thorough search "c" before implementing the missing person's procedure "a" or contacting the police "d." If you wait to see if he wanders back on his own "b," he could hurt himself badly.

Question 2   Answer: **c**

Explanation: Answer "c" is the only safe alternative. Just because you cannot see flames or smoke does not mean that there is not a fire. The fire brigade would rather be called out to a fire at this stage than to a blazing inferno. They will not be angry if it is a false alarm.

Question 3   Answer: **d**

Explanation: A carer who has not yet completed the lifting and moving course "d" should not be involved in the lifting and moving of clients. The drag lift "a" should never be used because it is likely to result in harm to the carers and/or the client. You are not qualified to teach the new carer how to move a client up the bed "b," and you should never try and lift a person up in bed by yourself "c."

Question 4   Answer: **c**

Explanation: Answer "c" is the most appropriate answer. Answer "b" is second best because it may be quite a while before these people can be released for the AIDS workshop. Answer "a" is simply an unhelpful comment. Answer "d" is incorrect.

Question 5   Answer: **c**

Explanation: Answer "c" is the correct, immediate, first-aid treatment for a burn.

Question 6   Answer: **a**

Explanation: If the person is hypoglycaemic as you suspect, the sweets will allow him to recover quickly. If the person does not quickly recover, call the doctor. All other options are highly dangerous.

MODULE 4

Question 1   Answer: **b**

Explanation: You must not undertake a clinical procedure unless you have the required clinical competence in that area of work—despite the department being short-staffed. Although the person-in-charge appears stressed, you are not going to help the situation if you make a mistake. You should develop the necessary competency at the earliest possible opportunity "b." You should not expect another member of staff to supervise you "c," so that you can start developing the necessary competence, when they are so short-staffed.

Question 2   Answer: **a**

Explanation: If there is any possibility that the sterile field has been contaminated, it must be changed. You cannot leave the wound uncovered. Therefore you should open up a sterile dressing, and temporarily cover the wound with it "a." You cannot temporarily cover the wound with the small sterile paper sheet that was provided as part of the dressing pack "c," as that also may have been contaminated by the water.

Question 3   Answer: **d**

Explanation: Jim has the right to refuse a shave and clean pyjamas. Whilst it would be appropriate to try and intercept Jim's sister "a" before she sees him so that you can inform her of the situation, the best approach is to telephone Jim's sister "d" and ask her to bring in some clean pyjamas for him, mentioning that he is choosing not to shave at the moment. This acknowledges Jim's rights to self-determination and overcomes the problem of him not having any clean pyjamas. You should not offer Jim counselling "c" when he is obviously not in the mood to talk.

Question 4   Answer: **a**

Explanation: The peripheral circulation of people who have long-standing diabetes can often be poor. This makes them susceptible to infection and slow healing whenever there is a wound on the foot. Therefore, if possible, all foot care (including care of the toenails) should be carried out by a qualified chiropodist or podiatrist "a." This is because some diabetic patients end up losing a leg because of poor foot care.

Question 5   Answer: **d**

Explanation: It may or may not be the tablets that are making Jill feel sick. But, whatever the reason, she has the right to refuse medication. It is essential, though, that the situation is noted in Jill's care record and that the doctor is informed so that he can consider prescribing an alternative medication for Jill "d." Tablets should not be left on clients' lockers "a" where they can be forgotten about or misappropriated by others.

Question 6   Answer: **c**

Explanation: It can be awkward for an able person to collect a midstream specimen of urine, even more so for someone who is disabled by arthritis "d." The specimen must be a midstream specimen, not the first sample passed by the client "b." It should be collected in a sterile container rather than a clean bedpan "a." Therefore, "c" is the correct answer.

Question 7   Answer: **d**

Explanation: There may be a very good reason for John's blood pressure to be raised (e.g., he has had hypertension for years and his blood pressure is often that high, he is anxious about a forthcoming operation). Therefore, it may not be appropriate to immediately inform the person-in-charge "a." Unless you are not sure about your blood pressure taking technique, it would be a waste of time to have your readings checked "b." These reasons for John's hypertension need to be excluded before you inform the person-in-charge of the problem "d." It is not appropriate to wait an hour before retaking his blood pressure "c." He could be dead by then.

MODULE 5

Question 1   Answer: **c**

Explanation: Confronting and threatening your colleague in the corridor "a" is not the best way to regain a positive working relationship with your colleague. If you ignore the problem "b," it is unlikely to go away. If you are friendly towards her and include her in all important decisions "d," she may stop being horrible to you. But she is more likely to think that you do not have the courage to confront her, and the snide remarks and mickey taking may get worse. The only way to sort out this problem, even though it is not guaranteed to work, is to approach your colleague in a friendly, but assertive, manner "c" to see if she is willing to sort things out.

Question 2   Answer: **a**

Explanation: If you listen carefully, but refuse to lay the blame elsewhere, and then insist that you plan together to overcome the problem "b," you are behaving autocratically. If this person does have a performance problem, it is not necessarily you who is the best person to sort this out with her. If you accept that the blame lies elsewhere "c," she shouldn't need another chance and a close eye kept on her. If you truly believe there is a performance problem, giving her another chance rather than getting to the root cause of the problem (e.g., bad temperedness), is not going to improve your colleague's performance. It is just a delaying tactic so that you can avoid having to tackle this person's poor performance now. Also, threatening your colleague with potential disciplinary action "d" will not tackle the cause of the problem. But, if you listen to your colleague attentively and clearly demonstrate where her performance has been substandard "a," she may be willing to work with you to overcome the problem.

Question 3   Answers: **b and c**

Explanation: If you think that you have nothing new to learn about the job "a," then you are probably in the wrong job. It is not appropriate to reflect on everything "d." The biggest portfolio is not necessarily the best one. You should reflect only on things that are important or significant to you or your clients. Both "b" and "c" are appropriate responses to your organisation's proposals for staff development and becoming a learning organisation.

Question 4   Answer: **c**

Explanation: Having reminded your manager that you have not had the chance to prepare for the appraisal "a," you should not give him the impression that you are willing to consider his proposed targets. These should only be negotiated after a full performance appraisal when both of you have had the chance to prepare properly and play an equal part in the appraisal process. Although your manager has not followed the organisation's appraisal policy, this does not necessarily make him a bully "b." It appears to be his workload and stress levels that are making him behave this way. Therefore, as long as you can negotiate to be more appropriately appraised at a later date when your manager has more time "c," it should not be necessary to inform higher management and increase your manager's stress levels. Just because your manager appears to be stressed out "d," does not mean that you have to accept his autocratic behaviour.

Question 5   Answer: **a**

Explanation: If the mistake is an error due to inexperience, it is appropriate to help her reflect on this experience to see what can be learned from it "a." If you threaten this person "b," or try to frighten her "c," this is likely to affect her confidence and does not guarantee that the same mistake won't be made again. Completing her level 2 NVQ award "d" may improve her confidence and competence. It may also make it less likely that she will make a similar mistake again. But, you want her to learn from this mistake, and the best way to do that is to reflect and learn.

Question 6   Answer: **d**

Explanation: If you look for alternative employment "a," or get a colleague to input your data "b," you are simply avoiding the problem. Although you are willing to attend the workshop in "c," it is not acceptable to just "do your best" at inputting data. Data input must be accurate if it is to be of any use. But, if you get a colleague to supervise you until you "get the hang of it" "d," your employer cannot ask much more of you.

Question 7   Answer: **b**

Explanation: It is not appropriate to reflect on the experience "a" when you have not yet come to terms with your feelings. At a later date, you may learn a lot from reflecting on this critical incident. If you simply get on with the job "c," this may not help you come to terms with your feelings, and your distress may be prolonged. It would not be appropriate to undertake a Suicide Awareness course "d" if you have not come to terms with your feelings. If you are still feeling distressed, the best way is to talk your feelings through with an appropriate person "b."

MODULE 6

Question 1   Answer: **d**

Explanation: It would not be fair to ask the consultant to allow the gentleman to jump the queue "a" when there will be many other individuals who are also desperately waiting for a hip replacement. It would also not be fair to hassle the general practitioner "b" who has no control over the waiting list. Unless the situation is desperate, it would not be fair to place the gentleman in a residential home "c," although the residential home could be used for respite care for the family. The best solution is to phone the Health Information Service "d." The general practitioner might be willing to send the gentleman to another health authority for his hip replacement, as long as the price of the hip replacement in the other health authority is not significantly higher than the local price.

Question 2   Answer: **b**

Explanation: If the home has an appropriate philosophy of care, it should not have a very strict routine and it should not try to exclude family and friends from providing care for residents. Therefore, you should not comply with the care staff's wishes "a." You could make a formal complaint "c," but this is likely to create a bad atmosphere and may not improve the situation. You may feel like withdrawing your relative from the home "d," but this might be premature if your relative is receiving good quality care and if the care staff are willing to show flexibility in involving you in the provision of care "b."

Question 3   Answer: **a**

Explanation: Until you are fully aware of his income and outgoings "a," you cannot plan a way forward to help this client. Until then, therefore, it would not be appropriate to help him apply for a Crisis Loan "b" or obtain a loan from the bank "d." No matter how well you know this client, it could be damaging to your relationship if you make a value judgment by advising him to spend less on tobacco and gambling "c." It is nothing to do with you how the client chooses to spend his money.

Question 4   Answer: **c**

Explanation: You cannot simply accept the word of the member of care staff "a" when there is a possibility that theft has taken place. The manager should be informed "b," but that does not necessarily mean that disciplinary action will be taken, especially if a genuine mistake has been made. If you confront the member of staff with the fact that you think he has stolen some of the client's money "d," then you are leaving yourself open to an accusation of slander because you have no proof. The best way is to re-visit the shops "c" to ensure that the money has actually been spent and to obtain copies of the receipts so that your organisation's financial procedures can be followed.

Question 5   Answer: **d**

Explanation: This information should be passed on to the appropriate authorities for them to handle "d." It is not your job to demand that the client stop making fraudulent claims "a" or that she quickly pays back all the additional benefits and allowances to which she is not entitled "b." Although you would like to maintain confidentiality "c," this is one of the few situations where your responsibility to your employer overrides the need to maintain confidentiality.

Question 6   Answer: **d**

Explanation: Telephone counselling "a" is a very specialised field of counselling for appropriately qualified and experienced counsellors. You may find it difficult to reassure this lady that she is coping well when it is obvious that she is not coping well at the moment. Asking her to contact her general practitioner is simply "passing the buck." The client appears to be in a crisis now, so promising to visit her within the next 10 days "b" is not meeting this lady's immediate needs. If you leave a message for her general practitioner so that he knows about the problem "c," again you are "passing the buck."

The only thing that you can do is ensure that you or another qualified and experienced care worker visits the client to assess her immediate needs "d." You can then plan to overcome the crisis which may include contacting the client's general practitioner or care manager to inform them of the situation so that a speedy resolution to the client's problem can be achieved.

Question 7   Answer: **a**

Explanation: You cannot remove the tablets from the woman's possession, without her permission "c" and "d," as the tablets belong to her. Their removal would constitute a theft. It is wholly appropriate that this woman should be allowed to self-medicate and keep her own tablets in her locker "a." You cannot insist that she fills out a chart "b" if she doesn't want to. Also, if you insist on counting her tablets, this could be construed as an invasion of privacy and might make it appear that you don't trust her.

MODULE 7

Question 1   Answer: **d**

Explanation: Answer "d" is the only option. Answer "a" is inappropriate because all lifting is to be avoided where possible. Answer "c" risks hurting both the client and you. Answer "b" cannot be right if the member of care staff is refusing to use the available slide sheets. You should inform your manager about the member of staff who is wanting to lift clients and who is refusing to use the available manual handling aids.

Question 2   Answer: **b**

Explanation: There is a wide range of normal frequency of bowel actions. For this girl one bowel action per week is normal, and it doesn't seem to be causing her any problems. Therefore, no assessment or intervention appears to be necessary.

Question 3   Answer: **b**

Explanation: Until a full continence assessment has been carried out, you cannot be sure what the problem is or how it should be treated/managed.

Question 4   Answer: **a**

Explanation: The only option that is a safe manual handling strategy, both for the client and the care staff, is "a." Don't forget to inform the person-in-charge of this problem and your chosen solution in case the client decides to complain.

Question 5   Answer: **c**

Explanation: As in question 3, until a full continence assessment has been carried out, you cannot be sure what the problem is or how it should be treated/managed.

Question 6   Answer: **c**

Explanation: Hopefully, you have got the message by now. As in questions 3 and 5, a full assessment needs to be carried out before you can devise a plan of care for this problem.

Suggested Reading

Benefits Agency (1998) **Bringing Up Children: A Guide to Benefits for Families with Children** (leaflet FB27). Department of Social Security: London.

Benefits Agency (1998) **Cash Help While You're Working: A Guide to Extra Help for People in Work** (leaflet FB4). Department of Social Security: London.

Benefits Agency (1998) **How the Social Fund Can Help You** (leaflet SFL2). Department of Social Security: London.

Benefits Agency (1998) **Sick or Disabled? A Guide to Benefits if You're Sick or Disabled for a Few Days or More** (leaflet FB28). Department of Social Security: London.

Benefits Agency (1998) **Social Security Benefit Rates** (leaflet NI196). Department of Social Security: London.

Bornat J, et al (eds) **Community Care: A Reader.** MacMillan: Basingstoke.

Cartwright S & Cooper CL (1997) **Managing Workplace Stress.** Sage: London.

Child Support Agency (1997) **For Parents Who Live Apart.** Department of Social Security: London.

Deasley C (1994) **The Care of Wounds.** Blackwell Science: Oxford.

Department of Health (1998) **Are You Entitled to Help With Health Costs?** Department of Health: London.

Getliffe K & Dolman M (eds) (1997) **Promoting Continence: A Clinical and Research Resource.** Balliere Tindall: London.

Griffiths-Jones A & Ward K (1995) **Principles of Infection Control Practice.** Scutari Press: London.

Karmi G (1998) **Ethnicity, Health and Society.** Blackwell Science: Oxford.

Loughran J J (1996) **Developing Reflective Practice**. Falmer: London.

Mallett J & Bailey C (eds) (1996) **The Royal Marsden NHS Trust Manual of Clinical Nursing Procedures** (4th ed). Blackwell Science: Oxford.

Resuscitation Council (1997) **The 1997 Resuscitation Guidelines for Use in the United Kingdom.** Resuscitation Council: London.

Royal College of Nursing (1997) **The Handling of Patients** (4th ed). RCN: London.

Royal College of Nursing & National Back Pain Association (1998) **The Guide to the Handling of Patients.** RCN: London.

Seed P & Kaye G (1994) **Handbook for Assessing and Managing Care in the Community.** Jessica Kingsley Publishers: London.

Soothill K, Mackay L & Webb C (1995) **Interprofessional Relations in Health Care.** Sage: London.

St John's Ambulance, St Andrew's Ambulance Association & British Red Cross (1995) **First Aid.** Dorling Kindersley: London.

Tadd V (1998) **Ethics and Values for Carers.** Blackwell Science: Oxford.

Taylor B J (1993) **Assessing Needs and Planning Care in Social Work.** Arena: Aldershot.

Thompson N (1997) **Anti-Discriminatory Practice** (2nd ed). MacMillan: Basingstoke.

United Kingdom Central Council for Nursing, Midwifery and Health Visiting (1992) **Standards for the Administration of Medicines.** UKCC: London.

Wilkinson R G (1996) **Unhealthy Societies: The Affliction of Inequality.** Routledge: London.

Wilson J (1995) **Infection Control in Clinical Practice.** Harcourt Brace & Co: London.

References

Brearley G & Birchley P (1986) **Introducing Counselling Skills and Techniques.** Faber & Faber: London.

Boud D, Keogh R & Walker R (1985) **Reflection: Turning Experience into Learning.** Kogan Page: London.

Department for Education and Employment (1995) **Disability Discrimination Act.** HMSO: London.

Department of Employment (1974) **Health and Safety at Work Act.** HMSO: London.

Department of Health (1992) **Health of the Nation.** HMSO: London.

Department of Health (1995) **On the State of the Public Health 1994.** HMSO: London.

Department of Health (1995) **The Patient's Charter and You.** HMSO: London.

Department of Health (1997) **The New NHS: Modern, Dependable.** HMSO: London.

Department of Health and Social Security (1983) **Mental Health Act.** HMSO: London.

Department of Health and Social Security (1986) **Disabled Persons Act.** HMSO: London.

Department of Health and Social Security (1968) **Public Health (Infectious Diseases) Regulations.** HMSO: London.

Department of Health and Social Security (1986) **The Health of the Nation.** HMSO: London.

Department of Trade and Industry (1994) **The Control of Substances Hazardous to Health Regulations.** HMSO: London.

Douglas A et al (1998) **Service Users' Perspectives on "Floating" Support.** Joseph Rowntree Foundation: York.

Equal Opportunities Commission (1986) **Guidelines for Equal Opportunities Employers.** EOC: London.

Health and Safety Commission (1987) **Violence To Staff In The Health Services.** HMSO: London.

Ironbar N 0 & Hooper A (1989) **Self-Instruction in Mental Health Nursing.** Balliere Tindall: London.

Marquis B L & Huston C J (1996) **Leadership Roles and Management Functions in Nursing (2nd ed).** Lippincott: Philadelphia.

Moody M (1990) **Incontinence: Patient Problems and Nursing Care.** Heinemann Nursing: Oxford.

National Health Service Estates (1995) **Health Guidance Note: Safe Disposal of Clinical Waste Whole Hospital Policy Guidance.** HMSO: London.

O'Kell S P (1993) **Managing Organisational Stress**, Part 1. Senior Nurse, 13, 3, 9-13.

O'Kell S (1997) **Older Patients - Who Cares?** Nursing Times, 93, 11, 37.

Parry G (1990) **Coping with Crises.** Routledge Ltd: London.

Robinson J R & Elkan R (1996) **Health Needs Assessment: Theory and Practice.** Churchill Livingstone: New York.

Tschudin V (1989) **Beginning with Empathy: A Learner's Handbook.** Churchill Livingstone: New York.

United Kingdom Central Council for Nursing, Midwifery and Health Visiting (1987) **Confidentiality: An Elaboration of Clause 9.** UKCC: London.

United Nations (1948) **Universal Declaration of Human Rights.** UN: Geneva.

United Nations (1971) **Declaration on the Rights of Mentally Retarded Persons.** UN: Geneva.

Wondrak R (1989) **Dealing with Verbal Abuse.** Nurse Education Today, 9, 276-280.

World Health Organisation (1948) **The World Health Organisation Constitution.** WHO: Copenhagen.

World Health Organisation (1994) **Basic Documents (40th ed).** WHO: Geneva.

Wright F (1998) **The Effect on Carers of a Frail Older Person's Admission to a Care Home.** Joseph Rowntree Foundation: York.

Glossary

A

abuse   physical, sexual, medical, or financial abuse, exploitation, or neglect

acidosis   disturbance of normal metabolism that causes body fluids to become more acid than normal

adopted role   set of behaviours and responsibilities taken on by a person who accepts a specified role (e.g., a new job)

advocate   someone who speaks up on behalf of, and for the benefit of, another person

alimentary canal   bodily canal into which food and drink is inserted at the top end (mouth) and faeces is excreted at the bottom end; digestion takes place along the way

angina   severe, but temporary, attack of cardiac pain, usually caused by exercise in people with heart disease

antibody   specific substance produced in the blood in response to being in contact with a foreign protein; antibodies have a role in the development of immunity

anus   end of the alimentary canal at the termination of the rectum; consists of sphincter muscle which allows the excretion of faeces

aphasia   difficulty using or understanding words

articulation   clarity of speech

ascribed role   set of behaviours and responsibilities that are assigned to a person because of his association with a specific group (e.g., an individual born into the royal household)

assault   unlawful personal attack

assertiveness   refers to confident and direct, but non-threatening and polite way of powerfully communicating with others in a positive fashion, without denying their rights

audit   formal inspection and assessment for the purposes of reporting and making recommendations for change

autoclave   machine that uses high pressure steam to achieve sterilisation

B

BP   blood pressure

bacteriocidal   describes any agent that destroys bacteria

battery   attack where an actual blow is delivered

bile pigments   constituents of bile which are produced by the liver and stored in the gall bladder; when emptied into the bowel, the bile pigments provide colour to the faeces

bilirubin   pigment largely derived from the break down of haemoglobin from red blood cells destroyed in the spleen

C

cardio-thoracic   pertaining to the chest and heart

catheter   hollow tube of variable length and bore that is used for the introduction or withdrawal of fluid from body cavities

cellulose   carbohydrate from the outer walls of plant and vegetable cells; cannot be digested by man and, therefore provides roughage

challenging behaviour   problem behaviour that is demanding and disruptive which makes it difficult to provide quality support and care

colon   large bowel

colostomy   surgically created opening between the colon (large bowel) and the surface of the abdomen

communication   act of conveying information to another person via signs, symbols, touch, or writing

complementary health services   examples include massage, osteopathy, acupuncture, aroma therapy, reflexology

confidentiality   non-disclosure of information in order to maintain the privacy/secrecy of spoken, written, or electronic facts

conjunctiva   delicate transparent membrane that lines the inner surfaces of the eyelids

contra-indication	sign, symptom, or illness that suggest that a treatment should be discontinued
crepitus	sound made when two broken ends of a bone scrape together
crisis	point in time when an urgent and stressful situation is overwhelming to a person
critical incident	important or significant experience that sticks in the memory
Crohn's disease	chronic inflammatory disease of the bowel
cystitis	inflammation of the internal wall of the bladder resulting in frequency and urgency in passing urine

D

data	accumulated information or facts
defamation	falsehoods (libel or slander) that result in damage to a person's reputation or character
defibrillation	controlled electric shock from a machine, applied over the heart, to try and restart it or to stop it from beating abnormally
dental caries	tooth decay
depersonal-isation	one effect on a person of an institutionalised environment in which there is little opportunity for individual expression (e.g., lack of personal possessions, no privacy)
discrimi-nation	perceived differences (usually showing a preference) between alternatives
disinfection	destruction of most micro-organisms on inanimate objects by using a disinfectant
diuretic	substance which stimulates the body to produce more urine
drug dependence	situation where an individual becomes psych-ologically or physically reliant on a drug being administered in order to prevent the appearance of withdrawal symptoms
drug tolerance	situation where increasing amounts of a drug have to be given to achieve the same effect

E

eczema	non-contagious skin condition which is often described as a reaction to an irritant by al-ready susceptible skin
empathy	ability to communicate to another person that you understand what he or she is feeling whilst demonstrating acceptance, respect, and trust
encopresis	incontinence of faeces
enema	injection of fluid into the rectum
enuresis	incontinence of urine, usually applied to bed-wetting
epidemiology	scientific study of distribution of diseases
eureka feeling	how an individual feels at the precise time when the person finally understands some-thing that is difficult, or has solved a difficult problem
evert	to turn outwards
exudate	fluid that oozes through the walls of small blood vessels
excretion	elimination of waste material from the body
expectoration	act of coughing up and spitting out lung secretions (sputum)

F

false documentation	entries in a personal record that are not true
flatus	bowel gas

G

granulation tissue	outgrowth of new blood vessels and connec-tive tissue cells from the surface of an open wound that is healing
gynaecology	pertaining to the female reproductive system

H

haematology	science relating to the formation, composi-tion, functions, and diseases of the blood

haemorrhoids	dilated blood vessels that grow inside the rectum; can make defaecation painful
halo effect	tendency to conform to others' expectations
hyperglycaemia	higher than normal level of glucose in the blood
hypoallergenic	very unlikely to cause an allergic reaction
hypochondriac	person who suffers excessive anxiety about his or her health
hypoglycaemia	lower than normal level of glucose in the blood

I

ileostomy	surgically created opening between the ileum (small bowel) and the surface of the abdomen
institutionali-sation	effect on a person who lives in an environment where there is rigidity of routine, block treatment, depersonalisation, and little opportunity to express individuality
interpersonal skills	ability to communicate and develop a rapport with other people
invasive	describes clinical activities that bypass the body's natural defences to infection

K

ketones	substances produced by incomplete metabolism which can cause acidosis

L

lacrimal apparatus	glands near the eye which produce tears, keeping the eye moist
label	classifying word or phrase that identifies something
learning style	personal preference for some methods of learning over other methods
lethargy	state of listlessness and lack of energy
libel	written, defamatory statement
lysozyme	antiseptic enzyme found in tears

M

meatus	opening at the end of a body passage or canal that leads to the outside
mental defence mechanism	mental distortion of fact to protect oneself from stressful thoughts and feelings
mentor	appropriately qualified and experienced practitioner who, by example and facilitation, guides, assists, and supports an individual in learning new skills and acquiring new attitudes
micro-biology	science relating to micro-organisms
micro-organism	living organism that can only be seen with a microscope (e.g., bacteria, viruses, some fungi)
micturition	act of passing urine
modulation	adjustments and regulation of the tone of voice during conversation

N

naso-gastric tube	tube that is passed up the nose and into the stomach for the purposes of removing fluid from, or introducing fluid to, the stomach
negligence	failure to give assigned care, or giving improper care that causes harm (e.g., failure to raise bed rails resulting in someone falling out of bed)
netelast	very flexible, tubular gauze that is used for holding dressings in place
nocturia	need to pass urine waking a person during the night
non-compliance	refusal to do what one has been asked to do
non-verbal communication	non-spoken information that is purposely or accidentally conveyed to another person during an interaction

O

oedema	abnormal swelling of tissues due to retention of fluid

207

ophthalmic	pertaining to the eye
orthodontic	branch of dentistry dealing with prevention and correction of irregularities of the teeth
orthoptic	relating to the study and treatment of eye muscle imbalances (squints)

P

paralytic ileus	paralysis of the muscle of the small intestine resulting in bowel contents not being able to pass onward, even though there is no obstruction
perianal	the area around the anus
peristalsis	wave-like movement of the muscles of the intestines which moves the bowel contents along the alimentary canal
prostrate gland	gland through which the urethra passes urine leaving the bladder
paranoia	delusions (false perceptions) of persecution
pathology	science related to the cause and nature of disease
peak flow	greatest amount of air that can be expelled from the lungs after taking the deepest breath possible
podiatry	care of the feet (chiropody)
prejudice	unfavourable opinion formed without proper judgement
psoriasis	chronic, non-contagious skin disease where inflamed areas of skin are covered in silvery scales

Q

quadriplegia	paralysis of all four limbs

R

radiography	process of imaging (e.g., x-rays)
rapport	harmonious accord; relationship that makes communication possible or easy
reflection	relates to a conscious process of thinking and interpreting experience in order to learn from it

right	legal and/or moral entitlement—legally or ethically due to a person
roughage	that part of food and drink intake that contains cellulose, providing bulk in the diet which stimulates peristalsis and the elimination of waste products

S

sacral area	skin and tissue above the sacrum at the base of the spine, on which you sit
sebaceous gland	glands situated at the base of hair follicles in the skin that produce the oily substance sebum
seizure	abnormal functioning of the brain, often including loss of consciousness, caused by abnormal electrical discharges within the brain
self-disclosure	divulging personal information to another person
service specification	document that precisely sets out the services offered by a service provider, including the quality of those services
skin flora	micro-organisms that have adapted to live on the skin of a host
side effect	any physiological change, other than the desired one, after administration of a drug
significant other	relative, friend, or someone who is important to that person
slander	spoken, defamatory statement
sphincter	circular muscle which can be contracted or relaxed to close or open a bodily orifice (e.g., anus)
spirometry	measurement of lung volumes of gas
sporicidal	lethal to the spores (seeds) of bacteria
stereotype	refers to a set of characteristics which are held to be common to members of a category
sterile	free from all micro-organisms

sterilisation	process of killing all living micro-organisms, usually by heat treatment
stigma	unpleasant or disgraceful characteristics attached to a person or group
stoma	opening
stress	unpleasant emotional experience linked to dread, anxiety, annoyance, etc.
stroke	physical condition where damage to the brain has impaired the function of one side of the body

T

TPR	temperature, pulse, and respiration
therapeutic relationship	enabling relationship in which a carer helps another person to meet his or her own needs
tumour	swelling caused by a mass of abnormal tissue which resembles normal tissue, but fullfills no useful function and can be harmful

U

unconditional positive regard	relationship in which warmth, acceptance, and empathy are freely given
ureter	duct that provides a passage for urine from the kidney to the bladder
urethra	passage leading from the bladder to the outside world through which urine is passed
urobilinogen	pigment formed in the intestine by the action of bacteria on bilirubin
urostomy	surgically created opening onto the surface of the abdomen through which urine can be voided

V

verbal communication	communicating by mouth (e.g., words, language, tone of voice)

Additional Words and Notes

Additional Words and Notes

Level 3 NVQ/SVQ Requirements

Mandatory Group A Units

- Contribute to the protection of individuals from abuse.
- Develop one's own knowledge and practice.
- Promote effective communication and relationships.
- Promote people's equality, diversity and rights.
- Promote, monitor and maintain health, safety and security in the workplace.

Option Group B Units

- Contribute to the development and effectiveness of work teams.
- Contribute to the development and review of care programmes.
- Contribute to the management of client continence.
- Contribute to the movement and handling of individuals to maximise their physical comfort.
- Enable individuals to administer their financial affairs.
- Enable individuals to find out about and use services and facilities.
- Prepare and maintain environments for clinical procedures.
- Prepare and undertake agreed clinical activities with clients in acute care settings.
- Promote communication with individuals where there are communication differences.
- Support clients during clinical activities.
- Support individuals when they are distressed.
- Support individuals in undertaking health care.
- Undertake agreed clinical activities with clients whose health is stable in non-acute care settings.

Note that most of the level 3 NVQ/SVQ units included within this workbook are also components of the old level 3 NVQ/SVQ in Care awards and some of them are also component units of other level 2, 3, and 4 NVQ/SVQ awards:

- Blood Donor Support (level 2)

- Care (level 2)

- Care (level 4)

- Caring for Children and Young People (level 3)

- Diagnostic and Therapeutic Support (level 3)

- Dialysis Support (level 3)

- Operating Department Support (level 2)

- Operating Department Practice (level 3)

- Health Care - Technical Cardiology (level 2)

- Health Care - Technical Cardiology (level 3)

- Health Care Physiological Measurement - Audiology (level 3)

- Health Care Physiological Measurement - Neurophysiology (level 3)

- Health Care Physiological Measurement - Respiratory (level 3)

- Promoting Independence (level 3)

The level 3 NVQ/SVQ in Care Award is part of the framework of qualifications leading to the Diploma in Social Work and is an entry qualification for people who would like to undertake nurse training or enter higher education.

It is essential to remember that you, as Care Support Worker, are under the indirect or direct supervision of qualified care professionals. A professionally qualified care practitioner must retain accountability for the assessment planning and review of care, for ensuring standards of care, and for determining the activity of support staff. It is important that you should not be expected or allowed to work beyond your level of competence.

Index